CCEA AS

PHYSICS

2nd Edition

COLOURPOINT
EDUCATIONAL

© Pat Carson, Roy White and Colourpoint Creative Ltd 2016

ISBN: 978 1 78073 097 4

Second Edition
Third Impression, 2021

Layout and design: April Sky Design, Newtownards
Printed by: W&G Baird Ltd, Antrim

All rights reserved. No part of this publication may be reproduced, stored in a retrieval system or transmitted in any form or by any means, electronic, mechanical, photocopying, scanning, recording or otherwise, without the prior written permission of the copyright owners and publisher of this book.

Page 224 constitutes an extension of this copyright page.

COLOURPOINT EDUCATIONAL

Colourpoint Educational
An imprint of Colourpoint Creative Ltd
Colourpoint House
Jubilee Business Park
21 Jubilee Road
Newtownards
County Down
Northern Ireland
BT23 4YH

Tel: 028 9182 6339
E-mail: sales@colourpoint.co.uk
Web site: www.colourpoint.co.uk

The Authors

Roy White taught Physics to A level for over 30 years in Belfast. He works for an examining body as Chair of Examiners for Double Award Science, Principal Examiner for GCSE Physics and Principal Examiner for A level Life and Health Sciences. In addition to this text, he has been the author or co-author of three successful books supporting the work of science teachers in Northern Ireland.

Pat Carson has been teaching Physics to A level for over 30 years in Belfast and Londonderry. He works for an examining body as Chief Examiner for GCSE Physics. In addition to this text, he has been co-author on a number of books supporting the work of Physics teachers at AS and A2 level.

Rewarding Learning

Approved/endorsed by CCEA on 1 May 2016. If in any doubt about the continuing currency of CCEA endorsement, please contact Heather Clarke at CCEA, 29 Clarendon Road, Belfast, BT1 3BG.

Whilst the publisher has taken all reasonable care in the preparation of this book CCEA makes no representation, express or implied, with regard to the accuracy of the information contained in this book. CCEA does not accept any legal responsibility or liability for any errors or omissions from the book or the consequences thereof.

This book has been written to help students preparing for the AS Level Physics specification from CCEA. While Colourpoint Educational and the authors have taken every care in its production, we are not able to guarantee that the book is completely error-free. Additionally, while the book has been written to closely match the CCEA specification, it the responsibility of each candidate to satisfy themselves that they have fully met the requirements of the CCEA specification prior to sitting an exam set by that body. For this reason, and because specifications change with time, we strongly advise every candidate to avail of a qualified teacher and to check the contents of the most recent specification for themselves prior to the exam. Colourpoint Educational therefore cannot be held responsible for any errors or omissions in this book or any consequences thereof.

Every effort has been made to ensure that practical work suggested in this book can be safely carried out in a school or college laboratory. However, it is the responsibility of teachers and lecturers to carry out an appropriate risk assessment when planning any practical activity. Where it is appropriate, they should consider reference to CLEAPPS guidance.

CONTENTS

Unit AS 1: Forces, Energy and Electricity

Unit AS 2: Waves, Photons and Astronomy

Unit AS 3: Practical Techniques and Data Analysis

Unit AS 1: Forces, Energy and Electricity

1.1 Physical Quantities

Students should be able to:

1.1.1   Describe all physical quantities as consisting of a numerical magnitude and unit

1.1.2   State the base units of mass, length, time, current, temperature, and amount of substance and be able to express other quantities in terms of these units

1.1.3   Recall and use the prefixes T, G, M, k, c, m, μ, n, p and f, and present these in standard form

Physical quantities

Physics is a science which relies heavily on measurement. To understand any physical phenomenon we have to be able to measure physical quantities. Examples of physical quantities include mass, length, time, force and energy.

To describe a physical quantity we first define a characteristic **unit**. To state a measurement of some physical quantity, for example force, we need to state two things:

1   Magnitude (size) – a numerical value

2   Unit

So a force of 25 newtons would be written as **25 N.**

International System of Units (SI units)

In 1971 it was agreed by the scientific community to use seven quantities as base quantities. This formed the basis of the International System of Units, abbreviated SI from its French name. In this system it was agreed that **only one unit** would be used to measure any physical quantity. However, multiples and submultiples of these base units or quantities are commonly used. Length is measured in metres (m), but multiples such as kilometres (km) and submultiples such as centimetres (cm) and millimetres (mm) are in common use.

Base units

The SI system defines seven base units from which all other units are derived. The table below shows the six base units that you will come across in this A level course.

Quantity	Unit	Symbol
mass	kilogram	kg
time	second	s
length	metre	m
electric current	ampere	A
temperature	kelvin	K
amount of substance	mole	mol

Prefixes for units

The table below lists the names of common multiples and submultiples of SI units.

Prefix	Multiplying factor	Symbol
femto	10^{-15}	f
pico	10^{-12}	p
nano	10^{-9}	n
micro	10^{-6}	μ
milli	10^{-3}	m
centi	10^{-2}	c
kilo	10^{3}	k
Mega	10^{6}	M
Giga	10^{9}	G
Tera	10^{12}	T

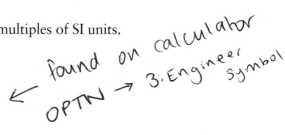

← found on calculator
OPTN → 3. Engineer symbol

Derived units

Many SI units are derived, i.e. they are defined in terms of two or more base units. For example, velocity is measured in metres per second, written as $m\ s^{-1}$. Some derived units have names, such as the newton (N) and the volt (V), but many do not.

The **name** of a unit when written in full is all in lower case, for example newton, joule and hertz. The **symbol** has a capital letter, for example N, J and Hz.

Do not add an 's' to indicate plural, for example 15 newtons is written as 15 N. If you write this as 15 Ns then you are stating that the physical quantity is 15 newton seconds and this is a measurement of impulse (momentum change) and not force.

Converting derived units to base units

It is sometimes useful to write a physical quantity in terms of its base units. Energy is measured in joules (a derived unit). What are the base units of energy? To calculate the base units for energy we can use any valid formula for energy, such as the following for kinetic energy, E_k:

$$E_k = \tfrac{1}{2}mv^2 \quad \text{(the } \tfrac{1}{2} \text{ has no unit because it is a number)}$$

In terms of physical quantities, we can write:

unit for energy = unit for mass × unit for velocity × unit for velocity

$$= kg \times m\ s^{-1} \times m\ s^{-1}$$

$$= kg \times m^2 \times s^{-2}$$

The base units of kinetic energy are therefore $kg\ m^2\ s^{-2}$. These are also the base units of **any form of energy** and of **work**.

Homogeneous equations

For an equation to be valid it is necessary, though not sufficient, for the units on both sides of the equality sign to be the same. Such equations are called **homogeneous**. Thus, the equation **force = (momentum change) ÷ time taken** is homogeneous because both sides have base units of kg m s⁻². On the other hand, the equation **pressure = momentum × volume** is **inhomogeneous** because the left hand side has base units of kg m⁻¹ s⁻², but the right hand side has base units of kg m⁴ s⁻¹. Inhomogeneous equations are nonsensical.

Exercise 1.1

1 Express each of the following physical quantities in base units.

   If the derived unit of this physical quantity has a name then state it.

   (a) Work   (Work = force × distance moved)

   (b) Power   (Power = work done ÷ time taken)

   (c) Momentum   (Momentum = mass × velocity)

   (d) Acceleration (Acceleration = velocity change ÷ time taken)

   (e) Force   (Force = mass × acceleration)

   (f) Frequency   (Frequency = speed ÷ wavelength)

2 On the planet Krypton the same laws of Physics apply as on the Earth. However, the inhabitants of Krypton have decided to use force (F), acceleration (A) and time (T) as their base units.

   What are the base units of energy on the planet Krypton?

3 A simple pendulum consists of a mass on the end of a length of string. If the length of the string is L and g is the acceleration of free fall, then the time to complete one oscillation, called the period, is T, where:

   $$T = 2\pi\sqrt{\frac{L}{g}}$$

   Show that the base units of both sides of the equation are identical.

4 A mass attached to a spring will oscillate up and down when disturbed. The period T of such oscillations is given by:

   $$T = 2\pi\sqrt{\frac{m}{k}}$$

   The mass is m and k is the spring constant, i.e. the force needed to stretch the spring by 1 m. The units of k are N m⁻¹.

   Show that the equation is homogeneous in terms of the base units on each side.

1.2 Scalars and Vectors

Students should be able to:

1.2.1   Distinguish between and give examples of scalar and vector quantities

1.2.2   Resolve a vector into two perpendicular components

1.2.3   Calculate the resultant of two coplanar vectors by calculation or scale drawing, with calculations limited to two perpendicular vectors

1.2.4   Solve problems that include two or three coplanar forces acting at a point, in the context of equilibrium

A vector is a physical quantity that needs magnitude, a unit and a direction.

A scalar is a physical quantity that requires only magnitude and a unit.

For example, speed is a scalar but velocity is a vector; mass is a scalar, but weight is a vector.

The table below lists some of the vectors and scalars that you will encounter in the AS course.

Vector	Scalar
Displacement	Distance
Velocity	Speed
Acceleration	Rate of change of speed
Force	Time
Electric current	Electric charge
Momentum	Kinetic energy
	Temperature
	Area
	Volume
	Mass

Combining vectors

When we add vectors we have to take into account their direction as well as magnitude. If the directions are in the same straight line then we can define any vector acting to the right as positive and any acting to the left as negative. When we add two or more vectors, the final vector is called the **resultant**.

For two forces of 15 N and 10 N acting in the same direction, the resultant is 25 N.

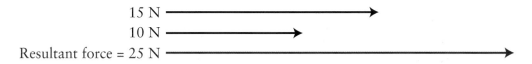

For two forces of 15 N and 10 N acting in opposite directions, the resultant is 5 N in the direction of the larger force.

15 N ————————————→
10 N ←————————————
Resultant force = 5 N ———→

Adding and subtracting vectors

If the vectors are not in a straight line then we use the **nose to tail method** to find the resultant.

The vector diagram on the left (below) shows two vectors, A and B. The resultant of these two vectors is C where **C = A + B**. The vector diagram on the right is obtained by placing the tail of vector B at the nose of vector A. The resultant, C, is the line joining the tail of A to the nose of B.

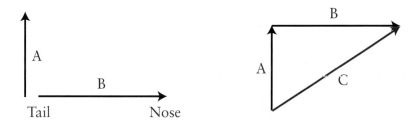

The resultant of subtracting the vector B from A is another vector, D, where **D = A – B**. The vector –B is a vector of the **same magnitude as B** but in the **opposite direction**. Effectively we add the negative vector, so **D = A + (–B)** as shown in the diagram on the right (below).

To emphasise that certain quantities are vectors, we sometimes underline them (A) or draw an arrow above them ($\vec{A}$) to show direction. In books, vectors are often shown in bold type (**A**).

Worked Examples

1   Linda moved 3.0 m to the east (AB) and then 4.0 m to the north (BC), as shown in the diagram on the right. What is her displacement from the starting point?

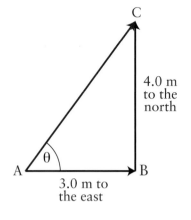

Solution

$AC^2 = AB^2 + BC^2$

$\qquad = 3^2 + 4^2 = 25$

$AC = \sqrt{25} = 5.0$ m

So although she has moved a total distance of 7.0 m, her displacement is 5.0 m (AC) from the start. Since displacement is a vector, a magnitude and a direction are both needed. So we also need to calculate the direction.

$\tan \theta$ = opposite ÷ adjacent = 4 ÷ 3 = 1.333 giving $\theta = 53.13°$

So Linda's finishing point has a displacement of 5.0 m from her starting point, at an angle of 53.13° to the north of east.

The above problem can also be solved using a **scale drawing**. For example, using a scale of 2 cm = 1 m, **use a ruler** to draw a horizontal line, AB, 6 cm long to represent the 3.0 m travelled due east. Now, from B draw a vertical line 8 cm long to represent the 4.0 m travelled due north. Suppose this vertical line ends at point C. **Join AC** to obtain the resultant displacement.

On the diagram AC will be 10 cm long, and with a scale of 2 cm = 1 m, it represents a real displacement of 5.0 m. Finally **use a protractor to measure the angle at C.** You should obtain an angle of 53° if sufficient care is taken.

2   The diagram on the right shows a canoe moving across a river at 1.5 m s⁻¹ while the water moves to the right at 1.2 m s⁻¹. If the canoeist sets off at A with the intention of rowing to B, he would not reach B, but would reach the opposite bank of the river at C. What is the canoeist's resultant velocity?

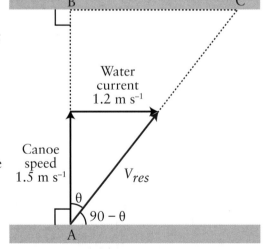

Solution

The resultant velocity v_{res} is the vector sum of the speed of the canoe and the speed of the water current.

$v_{res}^2 = 1.5^2 + 1.2^2$

$v_{res} = \sqrt{3.69} = 1.9$ m s⁻¹

The direction in which the canoe moves makes an angle θ with the line AB, which is perpendicular to the bank. So $\tan \theta$ = opp ÷ adj = 1.2 ÷ 1.5 = 0.8 giving $\theta = 38.7°$.

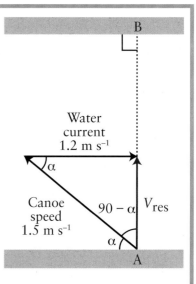

3 If the canoeist in Example 2 wants to cross from A to B, clearly he must paddle the canoe upstream. The direction in which he moves must combine with the speed of the river so that the resultant velocity is in the direction A to B. At what angle must he direct the canoe, and what is his resultant velocity?

Solution

The angle to the bank that he must now direct the canoe is α.

$\cos \alpha = \text{adj} \div \text{hyp}$
$ = 1.2 \div 1.5$
$ = 0.8$

Giving an angle $\alpha = 36.9°$.

The resultant velocity is then obtained:
$\sin \alpha = \text{opp} \div \text{hyp}$
$ = v_{res} \div 1.5$
$0.6 = v_{res} \div 1.5$
$v_{res} = 0.9 \text{ m s}^{-1}$

Components of a vector

It is often useful to split or **resolve** a vector into two parts or components. Each component tells you the effect of the vector in that direction. It is common to have these components act in directions that are perpendicular to each other, for example vertically and horizontally.

The diagram on the right shows a vector, F, that has been resolved into two components, which are at right angles to each other. The magnitude of the two components can be calculated as follows:

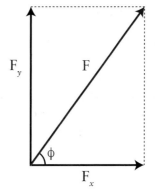

$\sin \phi = \text{opp} \div \text{hyp} = F_y \div F$
$\quad F_y = F \sin \phi$

$\cos \phi = \text{adj} \div \text{hyp} = F_x \div F$
$\quad F_x = F \cos \phi$

Equilibrium of forces

If we consider the forces acting in two perpendicular directions, such as up and down, left and right, then **the object is in equilibrium if the up forces equal the down forces and the forces acting to the left equal those acting to the right.** This is known as **translational equilibrium.**

Worked Example

1 The object in the diagram on the right is acted upon by three forces that make angles with each other as shown. Is the object in translational equilibrium?

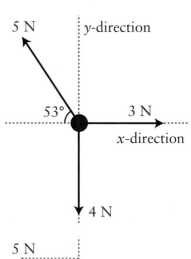

Solution

The object is in translational equilibrium if the resultant force is equal to zero. So to answer this question we must first resolve the forces in the x-direction and the y-direction.

In the diagram on the right the 5 N force has been resolved into its components, one in the x-direction and the other in the y-direction.

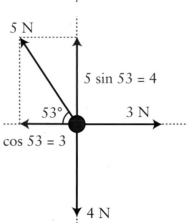

As you can see, the forces in the x-direction are equal and opposite, **and** the forces in the y-direction are also equal and opposite.

The resultant force is zero and therefore the object is in translational equilibrium.

Triangle of forces

Force is a vector. Each of the forces acting on an object can be represented by a line, the length of which indicates the size of the force and the direction of which represents the angle each force makes with the x and y directions.

When an object is in equilibrium the forces acting on it, taken in order, can be represented in size and direction by the sides of a closed triangle.

The phrase 'taken in order' means that the arrows showing the force directions follow each other in the **same direction** around the triangle.

The three forces in the worked example above are in equilibrium. This means that they can be represented by a closed triangle as shown in the diagram on the right.

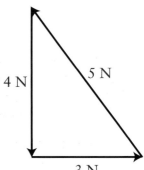

We sometimes need to find the force needed to restore equilibrium when two forces that are not perpendicular to each other are acting on a body. The magnitude and direction of this additional force can be found either by scale drawing or by calculation, where we resolve the vectors into their components and then add. The next worked example considers such a problem.

Worked Example

1 A force of 8 N acts due north and another force of 6 N acts at an angle of 45° to it as shown in the diagram. Find the third force needed to restore equilibrium.

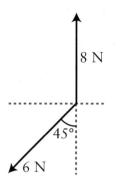

Solution

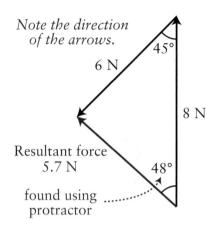

Note the direction of the arrows.

The resultant force can be found by using the nose to tail method discussed earlier, as shown in the diagram on the left. The force required for equilibrium is then one of the same size, but in the **opposite** direction to the resultant.

The resultant force (5.7 N) can be found by **scale drawing** and the angle measured (48°) using a protractor. Note that the resultant force is the line joining the tail of the 8 N force to the nose of the 6 N force.

The resultant force can also be found by **calculation** rather than by scale drawing. First resolve the 6 N force into a horizontal and vertical component as shown on the right.

The horizontal component is 6 sin 45°, i.e. 4.24 N, acting to the left.

Then calculate the vertical component. The 8 N and 6 cos 45° forces act in opposite directions. This gives an upward force of 8 – 6 cos 45° = 3.76 N.

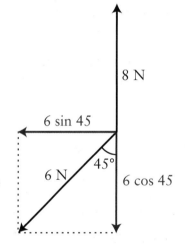

Pythagoras' theorem can be used to calculate the resultant since it forms the hypotenuse of a right angle triangle, as shown in the diagram on the right. The direction of the resultant force forms an angle ϕ to the vertical.

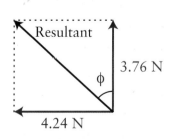

Tan ϕ = opposite ÷ adjacent
  = 4.24 ÷ 3.76
  = 1.127
 ϕ = 48.4°

So the resultant force is 5.7 N at an angle of 48.4° to the vertical.

Exercise 1.2

1 Using the vectors A and B, draw vector diagrams to show the resultant vector of each of the following:

   (a) **2A + B**

   (b) **A – 3B**

   (c) **–A – B**

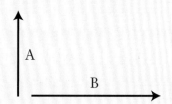

2 A cyclist starts from point A and travels 200 m due south to a point B.

At B the cyclist changes direction and travels 150 m due west to a point C, and then stops.

   (a) Calculate the distance the cyclist travels from A to C.

   (b) Draw a vector diagram, showing distances and angles, of the cyclist's journey.

   (c) Calculate the displacement of point C from point A.

3 An aircraft approaches a runway as shown in the diagram. A cross wind is blowing causing the pilot to maintain a heading at an angle θ if the plane is to land on the runway. The velocity of the cross wind is 2 m s⁻¹ and the aircraft's velocity, in still air, is 10 m s⁻¹.

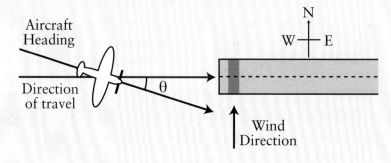

   (a) Draw a vector diagram to show the velocities of the cross wind, the aircraft and the resultant velocity of the aircraft.

   (b) Calculate the angle θ.

   (c) Calculate the resultant velocity of the aircraft.

4 A force has a vertical component of 23 N and a horizontal component of 14 N.

Calculate the magnitude of this force and determine the angle it makes with the horizontal.

5 A ship travels between three points A, B and C, as shown in the diagram. For the first part of the journey it sails due west a distance of 200 km. The second part of the journey is represented by the displacement vector S_{BC}.

   (a) By drawing a scale diagram find the value of the displacement vector S_{AC}.

   (b) Using the diagram determine the angle ϕ.

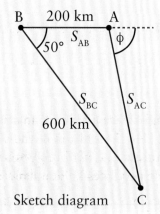

Sketch diagram

1.3 Principle of Moments

Students should be able to:

1.3.1   Define the moment of a force about a point

1.3.2   Use the concept of centre of gravity

1.3.3   Recall and use the Principle of Moments

Moment of a force

moment = Fd

The moment of a force about a point is defined as the product of the force and the perpendicular distance from the point to the line-of-action of the force.

moment = force × perpendicular distance from the point to the force

The force is measured in N and the distance in m.

Moments are measured in **newton-metres**, written as **N m.** The direction of a moment can be clockwise or anti-clockwise.

Worked Example

1 A mechanic tries to remove a rusted nut from fixed bolt using the spanner shown on the right. The spanner is of length 0.18 m. However, when he applies his maximum force of 300 N, the nut does not turn. By placing a steel tube over the handle of the spanner, the length is increased to 0.27 m. When the mechanic applies the same maximum force of 300 N at the end of the steel tube, the nut is just loosened.

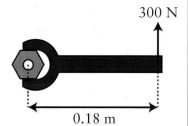

Calculate the minimum force that would have been necessary to loosen the nut if the length of the spanner had remained 0.18 m.

Solution

The moment required to loosen the nut is 300 × 0.27 = 81 N m. If the force required to loosen the nut, when the length is 0.18 mm, is *F* then:

$$F \times 0.18 = 81 \quad \text{Therefore } F = \frac{81}{0.18} = 450 \text{ N}$$

Couples

A single force acting on an object will make the object rotate and move off in the direction of the force. If **only** rotation of the object is required, a **couple** may be applied to the object. A **couple** is two forces that act in opposite directions, not along the same line, and which cause rotation. A couple produces **an unbalanced moment**.

Note: Study of couples is not required by the CCEA specification.

The diagram on the right shows a couple.

The moment of each force about the pivot is $F \times \frac{1}{2}d$.

The sum of these two moments is $F \times \frac{1}{2}d + F \times \frac{1}{2}d = F \times d$

The definition of the moment of a couple is:

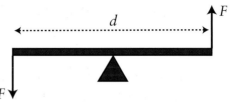

moment of a couple = one force × perpendicular separation of the forces

---

Worked Example

1 A coil is part of an electric motor. When it carries a current it is subjected to two forces that cause it to turn. The coil has a width of 10 cm and the total moment produced by the forces is 1.5 N m. Calculate the size of each force.

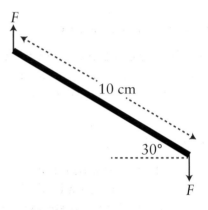

Solution

The pivot is the centre of the coil. To calculate the moment we need to calculate the perpendicular distance from the pivot to each force.

Total moment = one force × perpendicular separation of the forces

$$1.5 = F \times 0.1 \cos 30°$$

giving $F = 1.5$ N

Centre of gravity and centre of mass

This material is a recap of what you studied at GCSE. It is necessary to know this material in order to answer some questions on moments. At GCSE you may have learned:

The centre of gravity of an object is the point at which we can take its *weight* to act.

The centre of mass of an object is the point at which we take its *mass* to be concentrated.

This means that a resultant force acting through the centre of mass would cause the object to move in a straight line without causing it to rotate. For most everyday situations the centre of gravity coincides with the centre of mass: for everyday objects the strength of the Earth's gravitational field is the same for all points on the object. An object on the Earth would have to be very large – for example, a mountain – for the centre of mass and the centre of gravity to be in two different positions. Alternatively you would need to be close to a black hole, where the gravitational force changes by large amounts over short distances, to detect any difference between the positions of the centre of gravity and the centre of mass of an object.

The centre of gravity of a uniform beam (a beam whose width, thickness and composition does not change along its length) is at the mid-point.

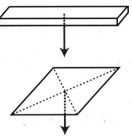

For a metre rule this would be at the 50 cm mark.

For a rectangular flat sheet (a lamina) the centre of gravity is at the centre, found by the intersection of the two diagonals.

Principle of Moments

The **Principle of Moments** states that when an object is in **rotational equilibrium, the sum of the clockwise moments about any point is equal to the sum of the anticlockwise moments about the same point.**

Worked Examples

1 A uniform metal beam of length 3.0 m weighs 100 N. It supports a load of 200 N attached to the end as shown. A steel cable attached to the beam keeps it horizontal and in equilibrium.

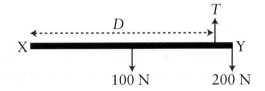

Calculate the distance from the end Y to the point where the cable is attached to the beam.

Solution

First we find the value of T. Since the beam is in equilibrium the resultant of the forces acting on the beam is zero. Therefore $T = 100 + 200 = 300$ N.

Second, we apply the Principle of Moments.

Taking moments about end of the beam marked X.

clockwise moments = anticlockwise moments

$$100 \times 1.5 + 200 \times 3 = T \times D$$
$$750 = D \times 300$$
$$D = 2.5 \text{ m}$$

Note that the question asked for the distance from the point Y.

Therefore distance from end Y is 3.0 – 2.5 = 0.5 m.

2 A wheel of radius 0.50 m rests on a level road at point C and makes contact with the edge E of a kerb of height 0.20 m, as shown in the diagram on the right. A horizontal force of 240 N, applied through the axle of the wheel at X, is required to just move the wheel over the kerb.

Find the weight of the wheel.

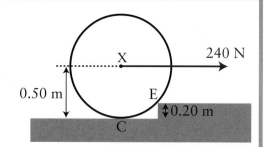

Solution

The first step is to mark the forces acting on the wheel not already shown on the diagram.

The weight of the wheel, W, acts vertically downward from the centre of gravity of the wheel, which is at the axle. The wheel is in contact with the kerb at E, so there is a normal reaction force R at this point (normal in this case means at right angles to the edge of the wheel).

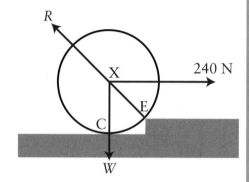

The wheel is just on the point of moving over the kerb, so it is in equilibrium. This means that the three forces acting on the wheel (the weight, the pulling force of 240 N and the normal force, from E) must act through the same point. This point is the axle of the wheel, X.

Taking moments about the point E means that we can ignore the reaction force R as it does not have a moment about this point (because its distance from E is zero).

The perpendicular distance from E to the 240 N force is 0.3 m.

The perpendicular distance from E to the line of action of the weight W is 0.4 m (by Pythagoras' theorem).

Taking moments about E:

$240 \times 0.3 = W \times 0.4$

giving $W = 180$ N

Exercise 1.3

1 A uniform wooden rod AB, shown in the diagram below, weighs 1.2 N and is 120 cm long. It rests on two sharp supports at C and D placed 10 cm from each end of the rod. Weights of 0.2 N and 0.9 N hang from loops of thread 30 cm from A and 40 cm from B respectively.

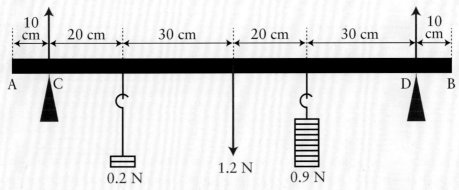

(a) Calculate the reactions at supports C and D.

   Hint: to find the reaction at C, take moments about point D.

(b) Comment on the sum of the reactions at C and D.

2 A uniform concrete paving slab has dimensions 750 mm × 600 mm × 75 mm and weighs 850 N.

(a) Calculate the minimum force needed to raise one end of the slab when it lies flat.

(b) Does it matter which side is used to lift the slab?

   Another uniform slab measuring 1500 mm × 900 mm × 25 mm also weighs 850 N.

(c) Is the minimum force needed to lift this slab larger than, smaller than or equal to the force calculated in (a)?

3 A uniform beam, AB, of length 8 m and weight 480 N rests on two trestles, C and D, placed 2 m from one end and 3 m from the other. A painter of weight 600 N stands on the beam directly over trestle C. The situation is shown in the diagram below.

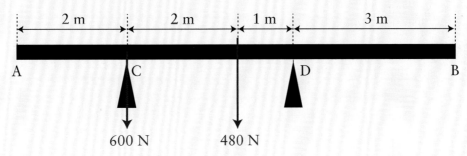

(a) Calculate the upward reactions at trestles C and D.

(b) The painter starts walking towards end B of the beam. What distance is she from B when the beam tips at trestle C?

   Hint: What is the reaction at C when the beam starts to tip?

(c) How far from A would the painter be standing when the beam begins to tip at trestle D?

4 To remove a nail from a wooden plank, as shown in the diagram, a force of 45 N must be applied at the end of the hammer. Calculate the force that exists between the nail and the wooden plank.

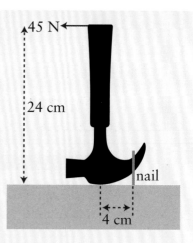

5 The diagram below is a simplified side view of a car bonnet, ABC, raised at an angle of 30° to the horizontal. The bonnet of mass 1.4 kg is hinged at A. Its centre of gravity is at B, the mid-point of AC. The bonnet is held in the open position by a vertical support rod DC.

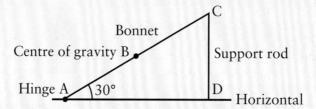

(a) Calculate the upwards force of the rod DC supporting the bonnet.

   Hint: Let the distance AD = d and take moments about A.

(b) The bonnet is now held open at an angle of 60° to the horizontal by a new, longer, support rod, again placed vertically at C. What is the upward force of the new rod supporting the bonnet?

6 A non-uniform metal rod weighs 300 N and is 2.5 m long. When pivoted as shown in the diagram below, it is in equilibrium when a force of 120 N is applied as indicated.

Calculate the distance from end X to the centre of gravity of the rod.

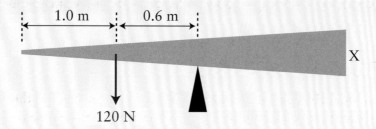

1.4 Linear Motion

Students should be able to:

1.4.1   Define displacement, velocity, average velocity and acceleration

1.4.2   Recall and use the equations of motion for uniform acceleration

1.4.3   Describe an experiment, using light gates and computer software, to measure the acceleration of

1.4.4   Interpret, qualitatively and quantitatively, velocity-time and displacement-time graphs for motion with uniform and non-uniform acceleration

Distance and displacement

Distance is a **scalar** quantity; it does not depend on direction.

Displacement is a **vector** quantity; it does depend on direction.

Displacement is the distance moved in a particular direction. An object that moves upwards can be said to have a positive displacement and one that moves down can be said to have a negative displacement.

For example, to travel from Cookstown to Belfast by car, you can take the road shown on the map. When you arrive at Belfast, the **distance you have travelled is 80 km.** However your **displacement**, shown by the dotted line, **is only 50 km in a direction east** of your starting point of Cookstown (distances and directions are approximate).

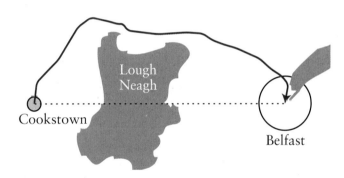

Speed and velocity

Speed is defined as the distance moved per second. It can also be defined as the rate of change of distance with time. Speed is a **scalar** quantity: it has magnitude (size) and a unit but not a direction.

$$\text{average speed} = \frac{\text{total distance travelled}}{\text{total time taken}}$$

Velocity is defined as the displacement per second. It can also be defined as the rate of change of displacement with time. Velocity is a **vector** quantity: it has magnitude (size), a unit and a direction.

$$\text{average velocity} = \frac{\text{total displacement}}{\text{total time taken}}$$

Speed and velocity are measured in metres per second, written as m s^{-1}.

Acceleration

Acceleration is defined as the rate of change of velocity with time. Acceleration is a **vector** quantity.

$$\text{acceleration in m s}^{-2} = \frac{\text{change in velocity in m s}^{-1}}{\text{time taken in s}}$$

Acceleration is measured in metres per second, written as m s^{-2}.

If an object is moving in a straight line and is slowing down, it has a negative acceleration. If an object is speeding up, it has a positive acceleration.

Acceleration is described as **uniform** when it is constant, i.e. equal changes of velocity take place every second. When the acceleration is **non-uniform** the changes in velocity that take place every second are not equal.

Displacement-time graphs

In the graph on the right the displacement increases by equal amounts in equal times. This means that the object is moving with **constant velocity.**

velocity = displacement ÷ time taken, therefore:

velocity = gradient of the line

In this case velocity = 40 ÷ 10 = 4 m s^{-1}.

The steeper the line, the greater the velocity.

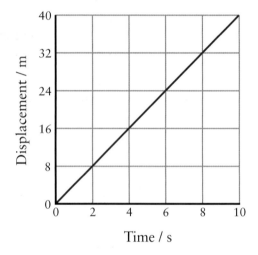

Velocity is a vector. A graph with positive gradient indicates a positive velocity. A graph with a negative gradient indicates a negative velocity. In this context, **positive and negative mean opposite directions.**

The displacement-time graph on the right shows an object that moves with a constant velocity of 4 m s^{-1} in one direction for 10 seconds, remains stationary for 4 seconds and finally moves in the opposite direction with a constant velocity of 6.67 m s^{-1} for 6 seconds.

The object has finally arrived back at its starting point; the overall displacement is zero.

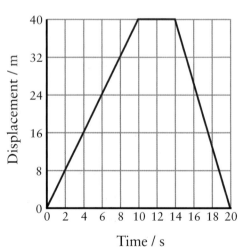

The displacement-time graph on the right tells us that the velocity of the object is increasing; it is accelerating.

The gradient of the curve at time = 0 is zero. This tells us that the object accelerated from rest.

The **average velocity** for the object is found by dividing the total displacement by the time taken.

In this case, the average velocity **over 4 seconds** is $16 \div 4 = 4$ m s^{-1}.

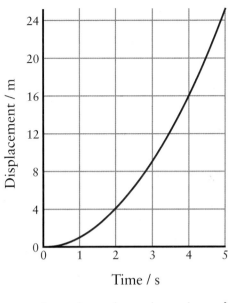

To find the **actual (instantaneous)** velocity at any time we need to carefully **draw the tangent** to the curve at that time and calculate its gradient. The tangent is a straight line that **touches** the curve but does not cut it.

For the graph shown on the right the instantaneous velocity at 4 seconds is the gradient of the tangent to the curve at 4 seconds.

$$\text{gradient} = \frac{\text{rise}}{\text{run}} = 16 \div 2 = 8 \text{ m s}^{-1}$$

It is worth noting that for an object undergoing uniform acceleration from rest, at any given time the instantaneous velocity at that time is aways **twice** the average velocity up to that time.

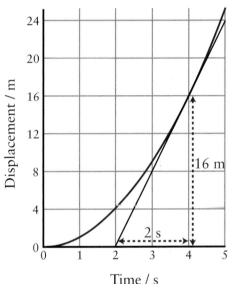

The displacement-time graph on the right shows an object moving with constant acceleration.

However, in this example the object does not accelerate from rest: it already has an initial velocity.

It is possible to tell this because the graph has a positive gradient at time = 0. In other words the tangent to the graph at time = 0 has a positive slope.

The gradient of this tangent is the initial velocity. It is approximately 4.5 m s^{-1}.

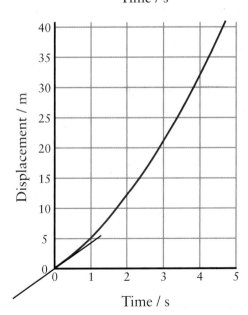

If the acceleration of an object is not constant (ie, it is non-uniform) the displacement-time graph is more complicated.

However, the **average velocity** at a particular time can still be calculated as:

average velocity = $s \div t$

The instantaneous velocity is equal to the gradient of the displacement-time graph at that instant:

instantaneous velocity = $\Delta s \div \Delta t$

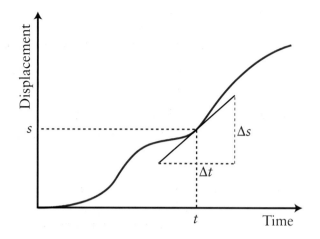

> **Note carefully that:**
>
> - the gradient of a **distance-time** graph represents the **scalar quantity, speed.**
> - the gradient of a **displacement-time** graph represents the **vector quantity, velocity.**

Velocity-time graphs

This graph on the right shows the motion of an object that is moving in a straight line and always in the same direction. It starts at rest, accelerates from 0 to 10 seconds, travels at constant velocity for 10 seconds, and then decelerates to a stop after a total time of 25 seconds.

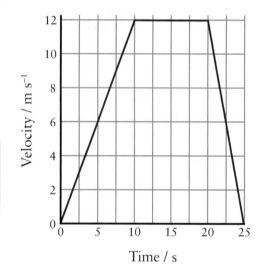

> **Note carefully that:**
>
> - the gradient of a **velocity-time** graph **gives us the acceleration or deceleration.**

Between 0 and 10 s the velocity change = 12 m s^{-1}
Gradient = 12 ÷ 10 = 1.2 m s^{-2}

Between 20 and 25 s the velocity change = −12 m s^{-1}
Gradient = −12 ÷ 5 = −2.4 m s^{-2}

This negative acceleration could be described as a **deceleration** of 2.4 m s^{-2}.

The steeper the line, the greater the acceleration. A positive gradient indicates acceleration. A negative gradient indicates a negative acceleration (deceleration). Straight lines indicate that the acceleration is constant or uniform.

Non-uniform acceleration

If the velocity-time graph is curved the acceleration is described as **non-uniform**.

The average acceleration at any time is the change of velocity up to that time divided by the time taken.

The instantaneous acceleration, i.e. the acceleration at any time, is found from the gradient of the tangent to the velocity-time graph at that time.

instantaneous acceleration = $\Delta v \div \Delta t$

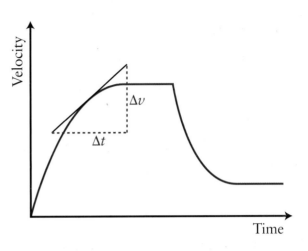

The velocity-time graph shown on the right is that of a parachutist. Just after she jumps from the aircraft her velocity increases rapidly; she has a large acceleration. However, as the velocity increases so also does the upward frictional force and her acceleration gradually decreases until she is moving with a constant velocity, known as the **terminal velocity**. The parachutist then opens her parachute and the velocity decreases rapidly until once again she is moving with a new, lower **terminal** velocity. The area between a velocity-time graph and the time axis gives the displacement.

Worked Example

1 Calculate the displacement from the velocity-time graph shown.

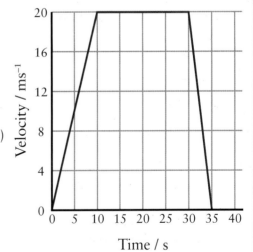

Solution

From 0 to 10 s:

displacement = average velocity × time taken
$\qquad$ = (½ × 20 m s⁻¹) × 10 (area of triangle)
$\qquad$ = 100 m

From 10 s to 30 s:

displacement = constant velocity × time taken
$\qquad$ = 20 m s⁻¹ × 20 s (area of rectangle)
$\qquad$ = 400 m

From 30 s to 35 s:

displacement = average velocity × time taken
$\qquad$ = (½ × 20 m s⁻¹) × 5 (area of triangle)
$\qquad$ = 50 m

So the total distance travelled in 35 s is 100 + 400 + 50 = 550 m, **which is the area of the trapezium.**

Varying velocity

If the object is experiencing a non-uniform acceleration the velocity-time graph is a curve, as shown on the right.

As before, the area between the graph and the time axis will give the displacement.

Equations of motion for uniform acceleration in a straight line

There are four equations that can be used to perform calculations when the motion of an object is one of uniform acceleration. You need not learn these derivations, but you need to remember the equations and know how to use them to solve problems. The following symbols are used in these equations:

u = initial velocity, v = final velocity, a = acceleration, t = time, s = displacement

Starting with the definition of acceleration, we can derive the relationship between initial velocity, final velocity, acceleration and time.

acceleration = velocity change ÷ time taken, or $a = (v - u) \div t$

Re-arranging gives us: $\qquad$ $v = u + at$ $\qquad$ (Equation 1)

Starting with the relationship between average velocity, displacement and time derive the relationship between initial velocity, final velocity, time and displacement.

average velocity = displacement ÷ time = $s \div t$

average velocity = (initial velocity + final velocity) ÷ 2 = ½$(u + v)$

Equating and re-arranging gives us: $\quad$ $s = ½(u + v)t$ $\quad$ (Equation 2)

Equations 3 and 4 are algebraic combinations of Equations 1 and 2.

Starting with Equation 2 we can eliminate final velocity using Equation 1 so that we end up with the relationship between displacement, initial velocity, acceleration and time.

$s = ½(u + v)t = ½(u + u + at)t$

gives $2s = 2ut + at^2$

and re-arranging we get: $\qquad$ $s = ut + ½at^2$ $\qquad$ (Equation 3)

We can use Equation 1 to eliminate time from Equation 3. This will give us the relationship between displacement, initial velocity, final velocity and acceleration.

$v = u + at$ and squaring both sides gives $\quad$ $v^2 = (u + at)^2 = u^2 + 2uat + a^2t^2$

Now take a factor of $2a$ out of the last two terms $\quad$ $v^2 = u^2 + 2a(ut + ½at^2)$

But from Equation 3, the term in brackets is s, so $\quad$ $v^2 = u^2 + 2as$

We have arrived at: $\qquad$ $v^2 = u^2 + 2as$ $\qquad$ (Equation 4)

Summary of equations of uniformly accelerated motion

Equation	Mainly used to find:
$v = u + at$	the velocity at a known time
$s = \frac{1}{2}(u + v)t$	the distance travelled after a known time
$s = ut + \frac{1}{2}at^2$	the distance travelled when the final velocity is unknown
$v^2 = u^2 + 2as$	the final velocity when the time taken is unknown

Remember: these equations only apply when objects are moving with uniform acceleration.

Vertical motion under gravity

An object dropped will accelerate due to the force of gravity. However, gravity is not the only force acting on a falling object. Air resistance or drag acts upwards opposing the accelerating force of gravity. **We can describe an object as being in 'free fall' if the *only* force acting on it is gravity.** All objects in free fall accelerate downwards at the same rate. **The acceleration does not depend upon the mass of the object.** The acceleration due to gravity, g, is approximately 9.81 m s^{-2}, but its value changes from one point to another over the Earth's surface.

Convention

It is convenient to adopt the convention that 'upwards is positive' when solving problems relating to motion under gravity. This means that an object moving vertically upwards has a positive velocity, while one moving vertically downwards will have a negative velocity. Similarly, objects above the surface have a positive displacement, while objects below the surface (such as those down a well) have a negative displacement.

Worked Example

1 A ball is dropped from a height of 10 m onto a hard surface and bounces a number of times. At the first bounce it rebounds to a height of 8.5 m. By making suitable calculations involving velocity and time, sketch a velocity-time graph for the motion of this bouncing ball to cover the time from release of the ball to just before it undergoes a second bounce.

Solution

Time to fall, from rest, from 10 m:

The ball moves 10 m towards the ground, so the displacement is −10 m. Since the acceleration is also downwards, g = −9.81 m s^{-2}.

$$s = ut + \frac{1}{2}at^2$$

$-10 = 0 + \frac{1}{2} \times (-9.81) \times t^2$ \qquad giving $t = 1.43$ s

To find the velocity after falling 10 m, use $v = u + at$

$v = 0 + (-9.81) \times 1.43$ \qquad giving $v = -14.0$ m s^{-1}

where the minus sign shows the ball is moving **towards the ground**. At this point, the ball undergoes its first bounce.

Initial velocity needed to reach a height of 8.5 m:

The ball is moving upwards, so the displacement and velocity are both positive.
But the acceleration due to gravity, g, is towards the ground and is therefore negative.

$v^2 = u^2 + 2as$

$0 = u^2 + 2 \times (-9.81) \times 8.5$ giving $u = \mathbf{12.9 \ m \ s^{-1}}$

Time to reach 8.5 m:

At this height the velocity = 0, but the acceleration is **still** $-9.81 \ m \ s^{-2}$ (even when the ball is stationary).

$v = u + at$

$0 = 12.9 + (-9.81) \times t$ giving $t = \mathbf{1.32 \ s}$

So the ball takes 1.43 s to fall 10 m from its original position and 1.32 s to reach a height of 8.5 m after its first bounce, a total of 2.75 s after it was first dropped. The ball then falls again, accelerating as it does. It will hit the ground, for the second time, after another 1.32 s (or 4.07 s after it was first released) with the same velocity as it left the ground after the first bounce. We can now sketch the velocity-time graph:

The first bounce is at 1.43 s. The direction of movement changes instantly from down (negative direction) to upward (positive direction).

The ball moves upwards, decelerating as it does. It reaches its maximum height at 2.75 s. It momentarily stops before falling, gaining an increasing negative velocity as it does so. Note that even when the velocity is zero at maximum height, the acceleration remains $-9.81 \ m \ s^{-2}$.

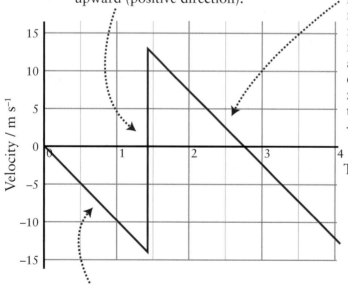

The ball accelerates uniformly at $-9.81 \ m \ s^{-2}$ as it falls. Note that the velocity and the gradient are negative, consistent with the convention. Velocity and acceleration are vectors, with downwards taken as the negative direction.

Experimentally measuring the acceleration of free fall using a light gate and computer software

Time intervals can be measured using light gates connected to a computer or data logger. The timer starts when the light beam is interrupted by an opaque object and stops when the opaque object has cleared the light beam. If the length of the object is entered into the computer or data logger the velocity of the object can be calculated by the software. If two velocities and the time interval between their measurements are known then the acceleration can also be found.

Method 1: Single light gate connected to a computer or data logger

This method is based on the equation of motion:

$$v = u + at$$

The width of the opaque strips is entered into the computer or data logger. Both strips should have the same width.

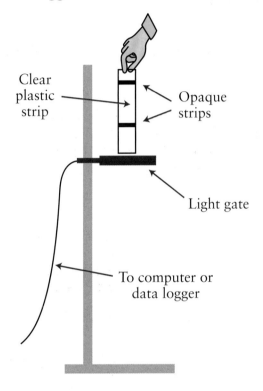

When the plastic strip is released, it drops vertically. The velocity (u) of the first opaque strip is measured, followed by the velocity (v) of the second strip. The time interval between the two strips interrupting the light beam is also measured. The acceleration of free fall g is calculated by the computer software as:

$$a = \frac{(v - u)}{t}$$

This method does not measure instantaneous velocities. The initial and final velocities are average velocities. The difference between the average velocity and the instantaneous velocity can be reduced by narrowing the width of the opaque strips. It is also good practice to repeat the measurement of the acceleration and take an average.

Tip: A small weight, such as a 100 g mass, attached to the lower end of the plastic strip will ensure that it falls vertically when dropped.

Method 2: Single light gate connected to a computer or data logger

This method is based on the equation of motion:

$v^2 = u^2 + 2as$

The object is dropped from rest a measured height above the light gate. The velocity of the strip is measured after falling this distance. Since the object is dropped from rest the initial velocity is zero.

The equation of motion then simplifies to:

$v^2 = 2as$

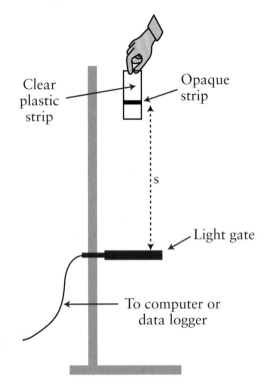

The width of the opaque strip is measured and entered into the computer or data logger. The distance that the plastic strip is allowed to fall is also measured and is recorded in a table or entered into the computer or data logger depending on the features provided by the software.

The plastic strip is released from a range of heights and the velocity is measured. It is good practice to repeat the measurement of velocity at each height from which the clear plastic strip is released. A table of results would have the column headings shown below.

Height of release s / m	Velocity 1 / m s⁻¹	Velocity 2 / m s⁻¹	Velocity 3 / m s⁻¹	Average velocity / m s⁻¹	v^2 / m² s⁻²

A graph of v^2 (y-axis) against s (x-axis) will produce a straight line which passes through the origin. The gradient of the graph gives a value of $2g$.

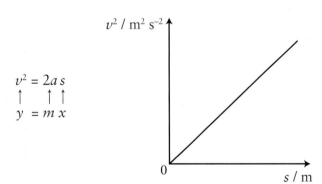

Exercise 1.4

1 A lift accelerates upwards at 0.5 m s^{-2} for 2 seconds then travels at constant velocity for another 8 seconds. It then decelerates uniformly to rest in another 2 seconds. It waits for 8 seconds to allow passengers to leave and enter before accelerating downwards at 0.5 m s^{-2} for 2 seconds. It then travels at a constant velocity for 3 seconds before coming to a rest in another 2 seconds. Draw the velocity-time for the motion of the lift.

2 The diagram on the right shows a displacement-time graph for a moving object.

(a) Explain how the velocity of the object at time t_1 could be obtained from the graph.

(b) What is the average velocity for the journey from the beginning to time t_2?

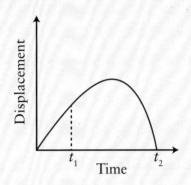

3 The diagram on the right shows a velocity-time graph for an object.

(a) Calculate the acceleration for the first 8 s.
(b) Calculate the distance travelled in 18 s.
(c) Calculate the average velocity during these 18 s.

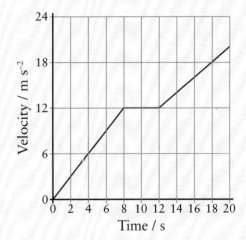

4 The graph on the right shows how the acceleration of an object varies with time.

It starts from rest and initially moves to the right.

(a) Calculate the velocity of the object after 1 s.
(b) Calculate the velocity of the object after 4 s and state in which direction it is moving.

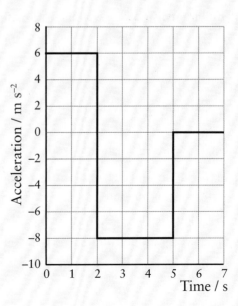

5 Opposite is a sketch of a velocity-time graph for a ball thrown up vertically from the surface of the Moon.

(a) Why does the velocity become negative after 3 s?

(b) Calculate the acceleration due to gravity close to the Moon's surface.

(c) Calculate the displacement after (i) 3 s and (ii) 6 s.

(d) Calculate the distance travelled after (i) 3 s and (ii) 6 s.

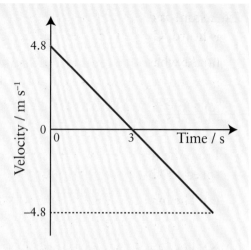

6 Competitor A in a cycle race reaches a point 60.0 m from the finishing line. He then travels with uniform velocity of 18.0 m s^{-1} in a straight line towards the finish. Competitor B reaches the same point (60.0 m from the finish) 0.100 s after A, travelling with the same velocity (18.0 m s^{-1}) as Competitor A. However, Competitor B then accelerates uniformly at 0.720 m s^{-2} until he reaches the finish.

(a) Calculate the velocity with which Competitor B crosses the finishing line.

(b) Make appropriate calculations to determine which competitor wins the race.

7 A ball bearing is allowed to roll, from rest, down a slope with a constant acceleration of 1.2 m s^{-2}. The slope makes an angle of 15° with the horizontal.

(a) How far down the slope has it travelled after 1.3 s?

(b) How far vertically has the ball bearing moved in this time?

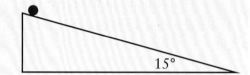

8 The Highway Code gives the following data for stopping a car.
Speed of car 80 km h^{-1}: thinking distance 15 m, braking distance 38 m.

(a) Convert 80 km h^{-1} to m s^{-1}.

(b) Use the thinking distance to calculate the reaction time of the driver.

(c) Calculate the value for the deceleration used in the data.

9 A ball is thrown vertically upwards with an initial velocity of 39.24 m s^{-1}.

(a) Write down (no calculations required) its speed and its acceleration when it reaches maximum height.

(b) Calculate the maximum height the ball reaches.

(c) How long does it take the ball to reach maximum height?

10 A stone is dropped from rest down a well. Exactly 5.00 s after the stone is dropped, a splash is heard. Give all answers to three significant figures.

(a) At what speed did the stone enter the water?

(b) Calculate the average speed of the stone as it fell.

(c) How far did the stone travel before it hit the water?

11 From the top of a tower 30.0 m high, a marble is thrown vertically upwards with an initial speed of 12.0 m s^{-1}. Calculate the following, giving all answers to three significant figures:

(a) The maximum height reached above the **ground**.

(b) The time taken for the stone to reach maximum height.

(c) The time taken for the stone to fall from its maximum height to the **ground** below.

(d) The speed of the stone when it strikes the **ground**.

12 A helicopter is at a height of 22.0 m and is rising vertically at 4.00 m s^{-1} when it drops a food parcel from a side door. Use the convention that 'upwards is positive'.

(a) Write down the velocity and acceleration of the parcel at the instant it leaves the helicopter.

Calculate the following to three significant figures:

(b) The maximum height reached by the parcel before it starts to fall towards the ground.

(c) The velocity of the parcel on impact with the ground.

(d) The time between the parcel leaving the helicopter and it striking the ground.

1.5 Dynamics

Students should be able to:

1.5.1   Describe projectile motion

1.5.2   Explain motion as being caused by a uniform velocity in one direction and a uniform acceleration in a perpendicular direction

1.5.3   Apply the equations of motion to projectile motion, excluding air resistance

A projectile is any object that is freely moving in the Earth's gravity, for example an object that is dropped from a height, or an object that is fired vertically upwards. These two examples have been dealt with in Exercise 1.4, questions 9–12 (pages 32–33).

Moving horizontally then falling over a cliff

We treat horizontal motion as one of constant velocity **since we are ignoring friction**. This means that whatever horizontal velocity the object might have had when it left the edge of the cliff, it does **not** change during its flight. When it leaves the edge of the cliff it begins to fall vertically. Its downward acceleration is 9.81 m s⁻². You treat it as an object dropped vertically from rest. Therefore, at any instant the velocity of the projectile is the resultant of:

(a) the constant horizontal velocity.

(b) the vertical velocity gained as it falls.

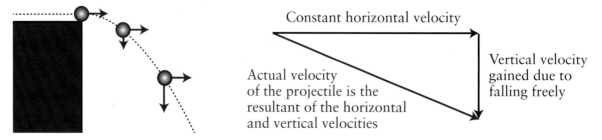

Constant horizontal velocity

Vertical velocity gained due to falling freely

Actual velocity of the projectile is the resultant of the horizontal and vertical velocities

A projectile fired at an angle to the horizontal

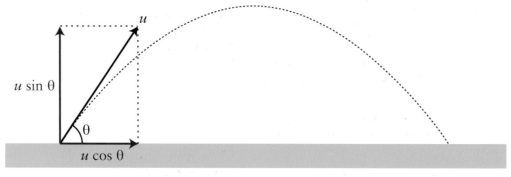

You treat this situation as follows:

1   Resolve the initial velocity into a horizontal component and a vertical component.

2 The horizontal component, $u \cos \theta$, does not change.

3 The vertical component $u \sin \theta$, decreases as the projectile moves upwards.

4 At the maximum height the **vertical** velocity is momentarily zero. The equation $v = u + at$ can be used to find the time taken to reach the maximum height since $v = 0$ at this height and u = initial vertical = $u \sin \theta$.

Note: that although the projectile does not have a vertical velocity (for an instant) at the maximum height, it **still** has a horizontal velocity.

5 The vertical component of the projectile's velocity increases again as the projectile falls. It takes the same time to fall from the maximum height as it did to reach it. The total time in the air is called the **time of flight** and equals twice the time to reach the maximum height.

6 The horizontal distance travelled is called the **range**. Assuming the projectile returns to the same vertical position:

horizontal range = constant horizontal velocity × time of flight

7 At any instant the velocity of the projectile is the resultant of the constant horizontal velocity and the changing vertical velocity.

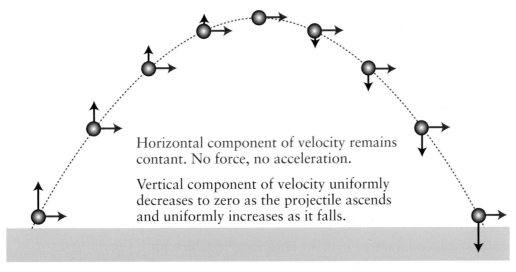

Horizontal component of velocity remains contant. No force, no acceleration.

Vertical component of velocity uniformly decreases to zero as the projectile ascends and uniformly increases as it falls.

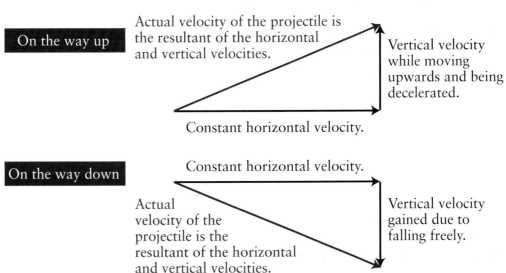

On the way up

Actual velocity of the projectile is the resultant of the horizontal and vertical velocities.

Vertical velocity while moving upwards and being decelerated.

Constant horizontal velocity.

On the way down

Constant horizontal velocity.

Actual velocity of the projectile is the resultant of the horizontal and vertical velocities.

Vertical velocity gained due to falling freely.

Worked Example

1 A stone is projected into the air from ground level with a velocity of 25 m s^{-1} at an angle of 35° to the horizontal. Calculate:

  (a) the time to reach the maximum height.

  (b) the maximum height reached.

  (c) the magnitude and direction of the stone's velocity 2.0 s after it was released.

Solution

  (a) At the maximum height the vertical component of the projectile's velocity is zero.

      The initial vertical velocity = 25 sin 35° = 25 × 0.5736 = 14.34 m s^{-1}

      Using $v = u + at$ we get: 0 = 14.34 + (−9.81) t

      Giving t = 14.34 ÷ 9.81 = 1.46 s

      Thus time to reach the maximum height = 1.46 s

  (b) The maximum height can be found in two different ways:

Method 1	Method 2
$s = ut + \frac{1}{2}at^2$	$s = \frac{1}{2}(u + v)t$
$= 14.34 \times 1.46 + \frac{1}{2} \times (−9.81) \times 1.46^2$	$= \frac{1}{2}(14.34 + 0) \times 1.46$
$= 20.94 − 10.46 = 10.48$ m	$= 10.47$ m

      The difference in the answers is due to rounding errors in the figures for u and t.

  (c) After 2.0 s the horizontal component of the projectile's velocity is 25 cos 35 = 20.48 m s^{-1}. Remember **the horizontal component remains constant throughout the motion.**

      After 2.0 s the vertical component can be calculated using $v = u + at$ where v = 14.34, a = 9.81 and t = 2.0. This gives v = −5.28. The minus is important, because it tells us that the projectile is now moving **down** with a velocity of 5.28 m s^{-1}.

      Draw the vector diagram showing both the horizontal and the vertical velocity at 2.0 s.

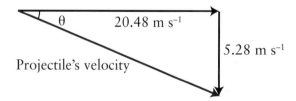

      θ   20.48 m s^{-1}

      5.28 m s^{-1}

      Projectile's velocity

Projectile's velocity = $\sqrt{20.48^2 + 5.28^2}$
$$= 21.15 \text{ m s}^{-1}$$

The direction of the velocity is θ: tan θ = 5.28 ÷ 20.48 = 0.2578
$$θ = 14.46°$$

Range

The **range** of the projectile is the horizontal distance it travels before returning to the ground.

range (R) = constant horizontal velocity × time of flight (T)

The **time of flight** is the total time the projectile spends in the air. In this time the projectile travels upwards to its maximum height and down again, taking the same time for each half of this vertical journey. The time of flight (T) is therefore twice the time it takes the projectile to reach its maximum height. At the maximum height the vertical component of the velocity is zero.

Using $v = u + at$, we find $0 = u \sin\theta - gt$, which gives $t = u \sin\theta \div g$

The time of flight $T = 2t = 2u \sin\theta \div g$

Thus, the range $R = u \cos\theta \times T = u \cos\theta \times 2u \sin\theta \div g = (u^2 \div g) \, 2 \sin\theta \cos\theta$

but, from the rules of trigonometry: $\sin 2\theta = 2 \sin\theta \cos\theta$, so:

range (R) = $(u^2 \div g) \sin 2\theta$

The range R depends on the angle of projection θ. $\sin 2\theta$ has a maximum value of 1, i.e. when $\theta = 45°$.

For a given initial velocity, the range R has a maximum value when the angle of projection θ is 45°.

Some angles of projection produce the **same range** but very different paths or trajectories. In general, the range when projected at an angle θ is the same as for a particle projected at an angle $(90° - \theta)$. So a particle projected at 30° has the same range as one projected with the same speed at 60°.

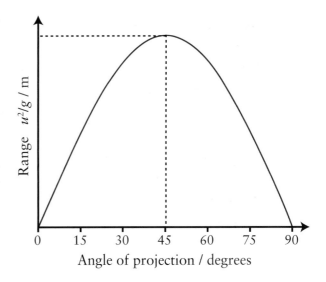

The diagram below shows the paths taken for some angles of projection.

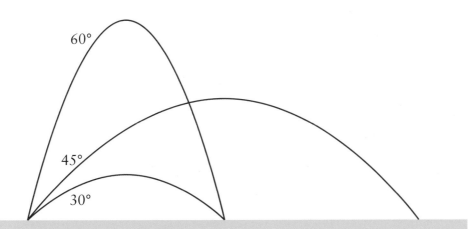

Exercise 1.5

1 A projectile is fired horizontally with an initial velocity of 20 m s^{-1}.

(a) How far does it travel horizontally in 3 s?

(b) Calculate the vertical distance it has fallen in this time.

(c) Draw a vector diagram to show the horizontal and vertical components of its velocity at this time.

(d) Calculate the resultant velocity at this time.

2 A shell is fired from a gun with a velocity of 100 m s^{-1}.

(a) Calculate the maximum range of the shell.

(b) Calculate the two angles of projection that would produce a range of 800 m.

3 An object is projected at an angle θ to the vertical. The initial velocity of the stone is V_o. The object follows the curved path shown in the diagram. At the point A on its path, the object has a velocity V. The direction of V makes an angle α with the horizontal.

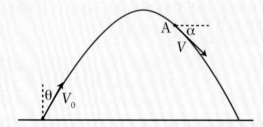

(a) Write down expressions, in terms of V and α, for the horizontal and vertical components of the velocity of the object at point A.

(b) Sketch graphs to show how the horizontal and vertical components of the velocity of the object vary with time from the moment the object was projected until it reaches point A.

(c) At what point in its motion does the object have the smallest speed? Write down an expression for this smallest speed.

1.6 Newton's Laws of Motion

Newton's laws of motion

Newton's first law of motion

If a body is at rest, it will remain at rest unless a resultant force acts on the object. If the body is moving in a straight line with a constant speed, it will continue to move in this way unless a resultant force acts on it.

The first law is another way of saying that all matter has a built-in opposition to being moved if it is at rest, or, if it is moving, to having its motion changed. This property of matter is called **inertia** (from the Latin word for laziness). The larger the mass of a body, the greater is its inertia, i.e. the more difficult it is to get it to move, to stop it moving or to make it change direction.

Newton's second law of motion

The acceleration of an object is inversely proportional to its mass, directly proportional to the resultant force on it and takes place in the same direction as the unbalanced force.

There are four ideas in this law:
- An unbalanced (resultant) force causes an object to accelerate.
- The direction of the unbalanced force is the same as that of the acceleration.
- The acceleration is inversely proportional to the object's mass.
- The acceleration is directly proportional to the size of the unbalanced force.

The car below has a mass m and is acted upon by a resultant force in the direction shown.

At time $t = 0$ the velocity = u At time t the velocity = v

So the acceleration of the car, a, is: $(v - u) \div t$

Newton's second law can be written: $F \propto ma$ (the sign $\propto$ means 'is proportional to') or $F = kma$, where k is the constant of proportionality.

The unit of force, the newton, is defined as **the force needed to cause a mass of 1 kg to have an acceleration of 1 m s⁻².** This means that the constant of proportionality k equals 1.

The consequence of Newton's second law, and the definition of the newton, is that we can write:

$\underline{F} = m\underline{a}$ where F = resultant force in N
m = mass in kg
a = acceleration in m s^{-2}

Some people like to underline 'F' and 'a' to emphasise that **force and acceleration are vectors in the same direction.**

Friction forces

Friction is a force that always opposes motion. Friction always acts in the **opposite** direction to the motion.

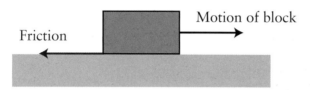

You need to be aware of the role of friction when determining a resultant force. This is illustrated in the worked example below.

Worked example

1 A car of mass 1750 kg accelerates up the slope at 0.4 m s^{-2}, as shown in the diagram on the right. The engine provides a forward force of 4200 N. Calculate the frictional force acting on the car.

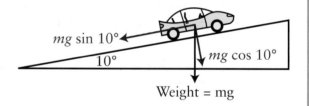

Solution

First, calculate the component of the car's weight acting down the slope.

This is mg sin 10° = 1750 × 9.81 × sin 10° = 2981 N

Second, calculate the resultant force, $F = ma$ = 1750 × 0.4 = 700 N

Third, resultant force = force of engine – component of weight acting down slope – friction

So: 700 = 4200 – 2981 – friction

Giving friction = 519 N

Newton's third law of motion

If body A exerts a force on body B, then body B exerts a force of the same size on body A, but in the opposite direction.

Forces come in pairs. If a hammer exerts a force on a nail, the nail exerts a force of equal magnitude but opposite direction on the hammer. One of these forces is called the **action force** (it does not matter which). The other force is called the **reaction force.**

You might think that if every force has an associated force that is equal in magnitude but opposite in direction, why don't they cancel each other out? How can anything ever get moving? The forces of an action-reaction pair **always** act on **different** bodies. This means they do not combine to give a resultant force and cannot cancel each other. Two forces that act on the **same** body are **not** an action-reaction pair, even though they may be equal in magnitude but opposite in direction.

For example, how does Newton's third law apply to an apple resting on a table?

The Earth pulls the apple down with a force F_{EA} (EA means 'earth on apple'). This is the weight of the apple and we could call this the action force.

The apple attracts the Earth with a force of equal magnitude but opposite direction, F_{AE} (AE means 'apple on earth'). Call this the reaction force.

F_{EA} **and** F_{AE} **are an example of the action-reaction pair of forces to which Newton's third law refers.**

The apple is also in contact with the table. The apple exerts a downward force, F_{AT} (AT means 'apple on table'). Call this the action force.

The table exerts an upward force on the apple with a force of equal magnitude but opposite direction, F_{TA} (TA means 'table on apple'). Call this the reaction force.

So F_{AT} **and** F_{TA} **are another example of the action-reaction pair of forces to which Newton's third law refers.**

If we look at the forces acting only on the apple, we have F_{EA} (weight of the apple) and F_{TA} (the upward supporting force from the table).

The forces F_{EA} and F_{TA} are equal in magnitude and opposite in direction but they act on the **same** body, the apple. Remember, these do **not** constitute an action-reaction pair because they act on the same object, in this case the apple.

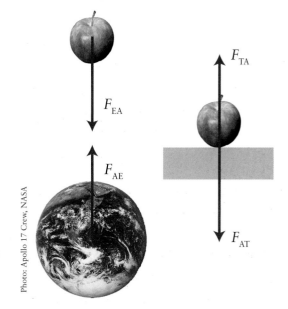

Photo: Apollo 17 Crew, NASA

Worked Example

1 A golfer hits a golf ball of mass 80 g. If the golf club is in contact with the ball for a period of 50 ms and exerts a constant force of 200 N, calculate:

(a) the acceleration of the golf ball and

(b) the speed of the golf ball at the moment it loses contact with the golf club.

Solution

(a) $a = F \div m = 200 \div 0.080 = 2500$ m s^{-2}

(b) $v = u + at = 0 + 2500 \times 0.05 = 125$ m s^{-1}

Exercise 1.6

1 A parcel of mass 6 kg slides from rest down a slope inclined at 30° to the horizontal. The friction force acting on the parcel is 4.95 N. Calculate:

(a) the resultant force on the parcel.

(b) the acceleration of the parcel.

(c) the distance travelled by the parcel in 2 s.

Take the value of g to be 9.80 m s^{-2}.

2 A motorist has a reaction time* of 0.6 s. While travelling at 20 m s^{-1} she sees a child suddenly run into the road 40 m ahead of her. The motorist applies the brakes to make an emergency stop. If the mass of the car is 800 kg and the average braking force is 6400:

(a) calculate the distance travelled during the reaction time.

(b) calculate the deceleration of the car when the brakes are applied.

(c) calculate the total distance travelled by the motorist between the instant the child is seen and the time the car comes to rest, assuming the deceleration is constant.

(d) is the motorist likely to collide with the child?

(e) comment on the effects of (i) alcohol consumption and (ii) driving in wet conditions on the overall stopping distance.

* Reaction time is time which elapses from the instant the brain receives a stimulus to the instant the brakes are applied.

3 A man of mass 60.0 kg stands on scales inside a lift. The scales measure the man's weight, not his mass. What readings would you expect to see on the scales when the lift is moving upwards with:

(a) a constant acceleration of 2.00 m s^{-2}.

(b) a constant speed of 2.00 m s^{-1}.

(c) a constant deceleration of 2.00 m s^{-2}.

Take the value of g to be 9.81 m s^{-2}.

4 A car of mass 800 kg tows a trailer of mass 100 kg. The engine force is 3400 N, the friction forces opposing the motion of the car add up to 400 N and the friction forces opposing the motion of the trailer add up to 300 N. Calculate:

(a) the combined acceleration of car and trailer.

(b) the tension in the tow bar.

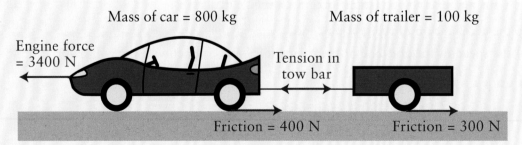

Mass of car = 800 kg   Mass of trailer = 100 kg

Engine force
= 3400 N

Tension in
tow bar

Friction = 400 N   Friction = 300 N

5   Masses of 3 kg and 2 kg are joined by a light string over a pulley, as shown in the diagram on the right.

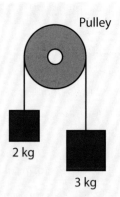

When released, the 3 kg mass falls towards the ground and the 2 kg mass rises vertically. Ignoring all frictional forces and taking the acceleration of free fall to be 9.81 m s^{-2}, calculate:

(a) the common acceleration.

(b) the tension in the string.

Hint: Treat each mass separately. Consider the weight and the tension for each mass. Form an equation for each based on $F = ma$ and solve simultaneously.

6   A large cardboard box has a mass of 0.80 kg. Its motion across a horizontal floor is opposed by a constant frictional force of 1.5 N and an air resistance force which increases with the speed of the box. The air resistance force, F_{air}, is given by the equation: $F_{air} = kv^2$, where the constant $k = 0.16$ kg m^{-1} and v is the speed of the box in m s^{-1}.

Patrick pushes the box across the floor with a force of 5.5 N.

(a) Sketch a large diagram to show all the forces acting on the moving box.

(b) Calculate the maximum acceleration of the box across the floor and state when it occurs.

(c) Calculate the maximum speed of the box when the forward force is 5.5 N.

1.7 Linear Momentum and Impulse

The momentum of a body is defined as the product of its mass and its velocity.
In symbols this is often written:

$p = mv$ where p is the momentum in Ns (or kg m s^{-1})

m is the mass in kg

v is the velocity in m s^{-1}

Note: momentum and velocity are vectors and take place in the same direction.

This kind of momentum is sometimes called **linear momentum**, because it relates to the momentum of a body moving in a straight line, as opposed to the momentum of a body rotating, like a spinning top.

Worked Examples

1 Show that the unit Ns is equivalent to the unit kg m s^{-1}.

Solution

From $F = ma$, we see that the unit of force, the newton, is equivalent to the kg m s^{-2}
So, the Ns = kg m s^{-2} × s = kg m s^{-1}

2 Calculate the momentum of a car of mass 800 kg travelling due North with a speed of 15 m s^{-1}.

Solution

$p = mv = 800 \times 15 = 12\,000$ Ns due North

Principle of Conservation of Linear Momentum

It can be shown experimentally that the total momentum of a **closed system** remains constant, even during collisions. By a **closed system**, we mean one where no external forces are acting. A closed system is therefore one in which the only forces which contribute to the momentum change of an individual object are the forces acting between the objects themselves.

For example, in a system of colliding neutrons, located far away from any other particles, the total momentum is conserved. Similarly, when two trolleys collide on a linear air track (where the friction force can be neglected) the total momentum before the collision is equal to the total momentum afterwards.

Or consider the collision of two balls on a snooker table. The collision occurs in an isolated system as long as friction is small enough that its influence upon the momentum of the balls can be neglected. In this case, the only unbalanced forces acting upon the two balls are the contact forces which they apply to one another. These two forces are considered **internal** forces since they result from a source within the system – that source being the contact of the two balls. For such a collision, total system momentum is conserved.

However during a collision between two cars on a road, where friction is large, the friction must be considered as an **external** force. This system of colliding objects is not closed and linear momentum is not conserved.

This allows us to state the **Principle of Conservation of Momentum** for bodies in collision:

If no external forces are acting, the total momentum of a system of colliding bodies is constant.

Collisions

When we apply this principle to collisions, it can be simply stated as:

Total momentum before collision = Total momentum after collision

As we shall see in the worked examples below, we must always remember that **momentum is a vector** and to **assign one direction as positive and the opposite direction as negative.** Thus if a car of mass 1000 kg moving at 5 m s^{-1} **to the right** has a momentum of +5000 kg m s^{-1}, then the same car moving at 10 m s^{-1} **to the left** has momentum of –10 000 kg m s^{-1}. The choice as to which direction is positive is entirely arbitrary.

Worked Examples

1 A toy truck of mass 400 g, moving to the right with a speed of 4 m s^{-1}, collides with and sticks to a toy tricycle of mass 1600 g moving to the left with a speed of 3 m s^{-1}. Calculate:

   (a) the momentum of each toy prior to the collision and

   (b) the velocity of the combination after the collision.

Solution

(a) Taking motion to the right as positive:

and motion to the left as negative:

Momentum of truck before collision = mv

$mv = 0.4 \text{ kg} \times +4 \text{ m s}^{-1} = +1.6 \text{ kg m s}^{-1}$

Momentum of tricycle before collision = mv

$mv = 1.6 \text{ kg} \times -3 \text{ m s}^{-1} = -4.8 \text{ kg m s}^{-1}$

Positive →

Negative ←

(b) By the Principle of Conservation of Momentum:

Total momentum before collision = Total momentum after collision

$\{1.6 + (-4.8)\}$ kg m s^{-1} = mass of combination × velocity of combination after collision

$-3.2 = (0.4 + 1.6) \times V_{after}$

$V_{after} = -3.2 \div 2.0 = -1.6 \text{ m s}^{-1}$

The minus sign shows that the **combined truck and tricycle is moving to the left**, that is, it is moving in the same direction as the tricycle was moving originally.

2 Two girls of masses 45 kg and 60 kg stand facing one another on light frictionless trolleys holding the ends of a strong taut rope between them. The lighter girl tugs the rope and starts to move towards her neighbour with a velocity of 2 m s^{-1}. Calculate the initial velocity of the heavier girl.

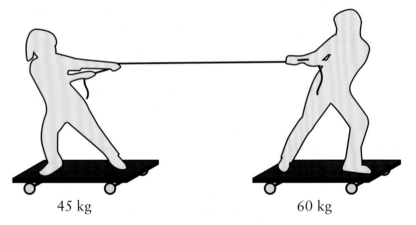

45 kg   60 kg

Solution

Assume after the rope is pulled the 45 kg girl moves in the direction of positive velocity, and the 60 kg girl moves with a velocity v.

Total momentum before motion begins = 0

Total momentum after rope is pulled = $45 \times 2 + 60 \times v$

By the Principle of Conservation of Linear Momentum, $0 = 45 \times 2 + 60 \times v$

Hence, $v = -90 \div 60 = -1.5 \text{ m s}^{-1}$. The minus sign shows that the 60 kg girl moves in the direction of negative velocity. So the 60 kg girl moves towards her neighbour at a speed of 1.5 m s^{-1}.

3 A bullet of mass 6 g is fired from a pistol of mass 0.5 kg. If the muzzle velocity of the bullet is 300 m s^{-1}, calculate the recoil velocity of the gun.

Solution

Momentum after firing = Momentum before firing

$(0.006 \times 300)_{bullet} + (0.5 \times v_{recoil})_{pistol} = 0$

So, $v_{recoil} = -(1.8 \div 0.5) = -3.6$ m s^{-1}

The minus sign indicates that the velocities of the bullet and the recoil of the pistol are in opposite directions.

Collision classification

Collisions may be classified as elastic or inelastic.

Elastic collisions are those in which kinetic energy is conserved. These only occur on an atomic scale, such as the collision of two molecules of an ideal gas.

Inelastic collisions are those in which kinetic energy is not conserved. Frequently, inelastic collisions involve kinetic energy being converted to thermal energy or sound. An example is the collision of a tennis ball with a racquet. A **completely inelastic** collision is one in which two bodies stick together on impact. Here the loss of kinetic energy is very large, though not complete. An example is a rifle bullet embedding itself in a sandbag.

Suppose a car of mass 1200 kg, moving at 10 m s^{-1}, collides with a stationary car of mass 800 kg and the two cars stick together. To calculate the speed of the two cars after the collision we apply the Principle of Conservation of Momentum:

Momentum before collision = Momentum after collision

$$1200 \times 10 + 800 \times 0 = 2000 \times v$$

$$v = 12\,000 \div 2000$$

$$v = 6.0 \text{ m s}^{-1}$$

Before the collision the total kinetic energy was $\frac{1}{2}mv^2 = \frac{1}{2} \times 1200 \times 10^2 = 60\,000$ J.

After the collision the total kinetic energy was $\frac{1}{2}mv^2 = \frac{1}{2} \times 2000 \times 6^2 = 36\,000$ J.

The collision has resulted in **a reduction of 24 000 J of kinetic energy. The kinetic energy is therefore not conserved.**

The **Law of Conservation of Energy** tells us that you cannot just 'lose' energy. Therefore this 24 kJ of **kinetic** energy must have changed into other forms. When the cars collide, a lot of kinetic energy is converted into sound and heat. So the 'missing' kinetic energy has actually been changed into these forms, and work has been done in changing the shape of the cars. But the **total** energy of the system **does not change**.

We can sum up these ideas in a table.

	Momentum	Kinetic energy	Total energy
Inelastic Collisions	is conserved	is NOT conserved	is conserved
Elastic Collisions	is conserved	is conserved	is conserved

Impulse

Newton's second law states that the acceleration a of an object is directly proportional to the resultant force F acting upon the object and inversely proportional to the mass m of the object. We can write this as $F = ma$.

Acceleration a is the change of velocity divided by the time t for the change.

If the initial velocity is u and the final velocity v then:

$$a = \frac{(v - u)}{t}$$

So we can write Newton's second law as:

$$F = \frac{m(v - u)}{t}$$

When both sides of the above equation are multiplied by the quantity t, we get:

$$Ft = m(v - u)$$

The product of force and time, Ft, is known as **impulse**. Impulse is equal to momentum change. The units of impulse are Ns or kg m s^{-1}.

Worked Examples

1 A golf ball of mass 45 g, initially at rest, is struck by a golf club. This causes the ball to move off with a velocity of 35.0 m s^{-1}.

The ball and the golf club are in contact for 4.0 ms.

Calculate the average force acting on the golf ball.

Solution

Using the impulse equation $Ft = m(v - u)$ we have:

$F \times 4 \times 10^{-3} = 45 \times 10^{-3} \times (35 - 0)$

$F = 393.75$ N

---

2   A snooker ball of mass 0.15 kg is moving with a velocity of 8 m s⁻¹.

It strikes the side of the snooker table at right angles and rebounds with a velocity of 6 m s⁻¹.

(a) Calculate the velocity change of the snooker ball.

(b) Calculate the impulse exerted on the ball by the table.

Solution

(a) Remember velocity is a vector: one direction is taken as positive, the other negative.
   The velocity change = 8 − (−6) = 14 m s⁻¹

(b) Impulse = momentum change = 0.15 × 14 = 2.1 kg m s⁻¹

Exercise 1.7

1   A projectile of mass m is launched at 60° to the horizontal with an initial velocity u. When it is at its maximum height it separates into parts A and B. Part A has a mass of $\dfrac{2m}{3}$ and part B has a mass of $\dfrac{m}{3}$.

After the separation, part A is momentarily stationary and part B is moving horizontally.

Deduce expressions, in terms of m and u, for the following:

(a) The momentum of the projectile before the separation.

(b) The momentum of part B immediately after the separation.

2   In an experiment to verify the Principle of Conservation of Linear Momentum, two bodies are caused to collide on a horizontal, friction-free track. Before the collision, one of the bodies, of mass 1.5 kg, is stationary, while the other, of mass 0.5 kg, moves with a speed of 0.18 m s⁻¹ to the right. Following the collision, the two bodies remain joined together, and move towards the right.

(a) Why is the experiment conducted on a friction-free track?

(b) This collision is an example of an inelastic collision. What is the difference between an inelastic and an elastic collision?

(c) Calculate the speed of the combined masses following the collision.

(d) Calculate the constant force F needed to stop the bodies in a time of 0.15 s after the collision.

3   Two frictionless trolleys, A and B, of mass m and 3m respectively, are on a horizontal track.

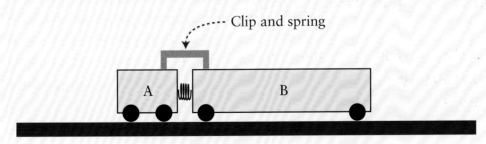

Initially they are clipped together by a device which incorporates a spring, compressed between the trolleys. At time $t = 0$, the clip is released and the trolleys move apart, the spring falling away. The time during which the spring expands is negligible. The velocity of B is then u to the right.

(a) Show that, as the trolleys move apart, the magnitude of the velocity of trolley A is $3u$.

(b) Calculate the kinetic energy of each trolley and the total kinetic energy of the system.

(c) Explain the source of the kinetic energy given to each trolley.

4 (a) Collisions between bodies can be classified as elastic or inelastic. In which of these types of collision is (i) linear momentum, (ii) kinetic energy and (iii) total energy conserved?

(b) Particle A of mass m, moving with velocity u, makes a head on elastic collision with particle B of mass M, which is initially at rest. After collision the velocity of A is v and the velocity of B is V. The directions of these velocities are defined in the diagram below.

For this collision express the conservation of momentum and kinetic energy in the form of equations, using the symbols used above for mass and velocity.

(c) For the collision shown above, it can be shown that:

$$v = \frac{(m - M)}{(m + M)} u$$

Use this result to find an expression for the ratio R of the kinetic energy of particle A after collision to the kinetic energy of A before collision.

R = kinetic energy of A after collision ÷ kinetic energy of A before collision

(d) For the special case in which the two particles are of equal mass ($M = m$) use the equation above to describe the motion of the two particles after collision. What is the value of R in this case?

(e) For the special case in which particle B is of infinite mass, use the equation above to describe the motion of the particles after collision. What is the value of R in this case?

(f) In a nuclear reactor uranium nuclei undergo fission when they absorb neutrons. To slow the neutrons down, to allow this absorption to take place, a moderator is used. The neutrons are slowed by head-on collisions with the atoms of the moderator. Use the equation above to show that graphite (carbon) is a better moderator than a heavy element such as lead.

mass of a carbon atom = 12
mass of a lead atom = 206
mass of a neutron = 1

1.8 Work Done, Potential Energy and Kinetic Energy

Work

When energy is transferred from one form to another it may be transferred by doing **work**. For example, when you lift an object you do work by transferring chemical energy to kinetic energy and gravitational potential energy. This concept of work gives us a way of defining energy:

Energy is defined as the stored ability to do work.

For example, when we say that a battery stores 50 000 joules of energy, we simply mean that the battery has the capacity to do 50 000 joules of work. But what do we mean by 'work'?

We define the work done by a constant force as the product of the force and the distance moved in the direction of the force.

Work done = constant force × distance moved in the direction of the force

or $W = F \times s$ where W = work done in joules (or N m)

                            F = constant force in N

                            s = distance moved in the direction of the force in m

At GCSE you did not pay much attention to the words 'in the direction of the force' used in the definition of work. But at AS level it is important that you recognise and can apply this new definition when the force and the distance moved are not in the same direction.

The following worked example shows why it is important to take into account the direction of the motion.

Worked Example

1 Consider an Arctic explorer dragging a sledge across a frozen lake. The explorer attaches the rope to his waist and the force of 200 N is applied at 30° to the horizontal. This situation is modelled in the diagram below. How much work is done by the explorer in dragging the sledge 150 metres across the ice at a steady speed?

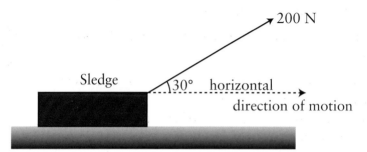

Solution

The difficulty here is that the force, F (200 N), and the displacement, s, are not in the same direction. The easiest solution is to resolve the 200 N force into its vertical and horizontal components as shown below.

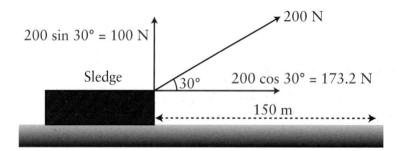

Provided the sledge does not rise above the ice, no work is done by the vertical force of 100 N. **Work is done only by the horizontal component of the applied force (173.2 N).**

Work done = constant force × distance moved in direction of the force = 173.2 N × 150 m

= 25 980 J

Notice that since the sledge is moving at a steady speed there is no resultant force, so there is a frictional force of 173.2 N acting to the left. This is why we say 'the explorer is doing work against the frictional force'. The situation described above occurs quite often and it is sometimes easier to use the general formula applicable when the force and distance moved are not in the same direction.

The general formula is:

$W = Fs \cos \theta$ where θ is the angle between the force and the direction of the motion.

To apply this formula to the sledge example above we would write:

$W = Fs \cos \theta = 200 \times 150 \cos 30° = 200 \times 129.9 =$ **25 980 J**

Potential energy

An object has gravitational potential energy when it is raised above the ground.

The gain in gravitational potential energy is equal to the work done in raising the object. If the object has zero potential energy when it is on the ground then the work done equals the amount of potential energy the object has when it is a height Δh above the ground.

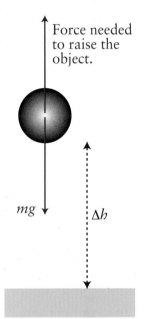

Force needed to raise the object.

If the object of mass m is raised a distance Δh then the amount of work done in raising the object is:

Work done = force needed × distance moved in direction of this force
  = weight × vertical distance moved
  = $mg\Delta h$ (where g is the acceleration of free fall)
  = gain in gravitational potential energy

$\Delta p.e. = mg\Delta h$ where $\Delta p.e.$ = change in potential energy in J
          m = mass in kg
          g = acceleration of free fall
          Δh = vertical distance moved in m

Kinetic energy

A moving object possesses kinetic energy.

Consider an object of mass m, initially at rest. It is acted upon by a resultant force F and the object accelerates. This force acts over a distance s. Having travelled this distance the object has a velocity v.

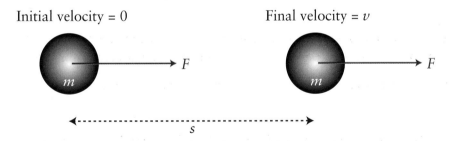

Initial velocity = 0   Final velocity = v

Work done in moving the object a distance s is $W = F \times s$.

Newton's second law ($F = ma$) allows us to replace F in this expression, giving $W = ma \times s$.

The equation of motion $v^2 = u^2 + 2as$ allows us to introduce velocity into our expression for W. The initial velocity of this object was 0, so: $as = \frac{1}{2}v^2$. Hence:

$k.e. = \frac{1}{2}mv^2$ where $k.e.$ = kinetic energy in J
          m = mass in kg
          v = velocity in m s^{-1}

In general the work done on an object is equal to the **change** in the kinetic energy of the object. If the final speed v is greater than the initial speed u then W is the work done in accelerating the object over a distance s. If the final speed v is less than the initial speed u then W is the work done in slowing the object down over a distance s.

$W = \frac{1}{2}mv^2 - \frac{1}{2}mu^2$ where W = work done in J
m = mass in kg
v = final velocity in m s^{-1}
u = initial velocity in m s^{-1}

Principle of Conservation of Energy

The Principle of Conservation of Energy states that energy cannot be created or destroyed but can be changed from one form to another.

Some forms of energy are more useful than others: some are more suitable for doing work and for being changed into other forms of energy. Electrical and chemical energy are in this category and are sometimes known as high-grade forms of energy.

On the other hand, internal energy – for example the kinetic energy of gas molecules due to their random motion – is a low-grade form of energy that is not easily converted into other forms.

The Principle of Conservation of Energy as it applies to a falling object

An object held above the ground and then released will gradually convert potential energy to kinetic energy. At any time its total energy (E_T), i.e. the sum of its kinetic (E_k) and potential (E_p) energies, is constant. At any point along its path, as it falls, the total energy E_T is also constant.

How do the kinetic energy and the potential energy vary as it falls?

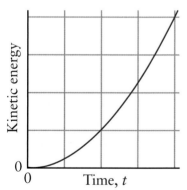

As the object accelerates from rest ($u = 0$) its velocity at any instant is $v = at$, so:

$E_k = \frac{1}{2}mv^2 = \frac{1}{2} ma^2t^2$

E_k is proportional to t^2.

As the object falls its E_p decreases. At any instant the E_p equals the initial potential energy (E_T) less the kinetic energy (E_k), so:

$E_p = E_T - E_k$

$E_p = E_T - \frac{1}{2} ma^2t^2$

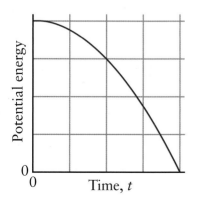

These relationships are illustrated by the graphs on the right.

If the object falls a distance y then its potential energy at this point is:

$$E_p = E_T - mgy$$

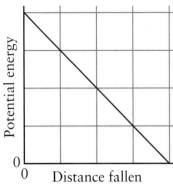

As the object falls a distance y we can use the equation of motion $v^2 = u^2 + 2as$ to find its velocity at this point. This gives $v^2 = 2gy$.

$E_k = \frac{1}{2}mv^2$ but we can substitute, giving

$E_k = mgy$

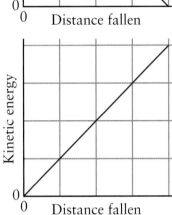

The following examples show the strength of using energy interchange to solve problems in mechanics.

Worked Examples

1 Masses of 6.0 kg and 2.0 kg are connected by a light inextensible string passing over a smooth pulley. The string is taut when the masses are released. The smaller mass accelerates upwards and the bigger mass accelerates downwards. Using the Principle of Conservation of Energy, calculate the speed of the masses when the larger one has descended 2.0 m.

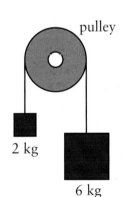

Solution

The 2.0 kg mass is accelerating upwards and is gaining both kinetic and potential energy. The 6.0 kg mass is accelerating downwards and is gaining kinetic energy and losing potential energy.

Let the speed of each mass be v (in m s^{-1}) when the larger one has descended 2.0 m.

Net loss in energy of 6.0 kg mass $= p.e. - k.e. = mgh - \frac{1}{2}mv^2 = (6 \times g \times 2) - (\frac{1}{2} \times 6 \times v^2)$
$$= 12g - 3v^2$$

Net gain in energy of 2.0 kg mass $= p.e. + k.e. = mgh + \frac{1}{2}mv^2 = (2 \times g \times 2) + (\frac{1}{2} \times 2 \times v^2)$
$$= 4g + v^2$$

By the Principle of Conservation of Energy:
the net loss in energy of the 6.0 kg mass = net gain in energy of the 2.0 kg mass, so:

$12g - 3v^2 = 4g + v^2$ which rearranges to give

    $8g = 4v^2$ which simplifies to

    $v = \sqrt{(2g)} = \sqrt{(2 \times 9.81)} = \mathbf{4.4\ m\ s^{-1}}$

An equally valid approach is to use the idea that the total loss in p.e. is equal to the total gain in k.e.

This leads to:

Loss in p.e. = $(mgh)_{\text{for 6 kg mass}} - (mgh)_{\text{for 2 kg mass}} = (6 \times g \times 2) - (2 \times g \times 2) = 8g$

Gain in k.e. = $(\tfrac{1}{2}mv^2)_{\text{for 6 kg mass}} + (\tfrac{1}{2}mv^2)_{\text{for 2 kg mass}} = (\tfrac{1}{2} \times 6 \times v^2) + (\tfrac{1}{2} \times 2 \times v^2) = 4v^2$

Hence, $8g = 4v^2$, which simplifies as above to give $v = \textbf{4.4 m s}^{-1}$

> **Note:** This problem can also be solved by first finding the common acceleration of the masses and then applying Newton's equations of uniform acceleration.

2 A small block of wood passes through point P at a speed of 2.00 m s⁻¹ and slides down a smooth curved track.

   (a) Calculate the speed of the block as it passes point Q, 12.0 m vertically below P.

   (b) Explain why it would be inappropriate to use Newton's equations of uniform acceleration in this situation.

   (c) Does the time taken to travel from P to Q depend on the equation of the curved slope? Explain your answer.

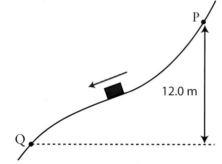

Solution

   (a) Let the speed of the block as it passes Q be v.

   By the Principle of Conservation of Energy:

$$\text{loss in gravitational } p.e. = \text{gain in } k.e.$$
$$mg\Delta h = \tfrac{1}{2}mv^2 - \tfrac{1}{2}mu^2$$

   Substituting: $m \times 9.81 \times 12 = \tfrac{1}{2}mv^2 - \tfrac{1}{2}mu^2$

   cancelling m: $117.72 = \tfrac{1}{2}(v^2 - 2^2)$

   and solving: $v = 15.5 \text{ m s}^{-1}$

   (b) The acceleration is not uniform (and not in a straight line).

   (c) Yes. The steeper the slope the greater the average acceleration and the smaller the time taken.

Power

Power is defined as the rate of doing work.

The definition can be expressed as an equation:

$$\textbf{Power} = \frac{\textbf{Work done}}{\textbf{Time taken}}$$

or $P = \dfrac{W}{t}$ where P = power in watts (W) or joules per second (J s⁻¹)

W = work done in joules (J)

t = time taken in seconds (s)

If the work is being done by a **constant** force, F, then we know that the work done, W, can be written as $W = Fs$. Making this substitution for W in the power equation gives $P = Fs \div t$. If the **displacement occurs at a steady rate**, then speed $v = s \div t$ and we arrive at:

$P = Fv$ where P = power in watts (W) or joules per second (J s^{-1})
         F = force being applied in newtons (N)
         v = constant speed at which force is moving (m s^{-1})

Worked Examples

1 An electric motor has an output power of 2400 W and is used to raise a ship's anchor. If the tension in the cable is 8 kN, at what constant speed is the anchor being raised?

   Solution

   $P = Fv$, so $v = P \div F = 2400 \div 8000 =$ **0.3 m s^{-1}**

2 A car of mass 1200 kg has an output power of 60 kW when travelling at a speed of 30 m s^{-1} along a flat road. What power output is required if the same car is to travel at the same speed up a hill of gradient 10%? (Such a hill has an angle of slope of $\tan^{-1}(0.1)$ or 5.7°.)

   Students are advised to re-visit the material on resolution of forces on the inclined plane (page 40) before attempting this question. Take g as 9.81 m s^{-2}.

   Solution

   Additional force to be overcome due to hill = $mg.\sin\theta = 1200 \times g \times \sin 5.7° = 1169.19$ N
   Additional power required = $Fv = 1169.19 \times 30 = 35\,076$ W ≈ 35 kW
   Total power required = 60 + 35 = 95 kW

3 The engine of a motor boat delivers 36 kW to the propeller while the boat is moving at a constant 9 m s^{-1}. Calculate the tension in the tow rope if, instead of using its engine, the boat were being towed at the same speed.

   Solution

   Force (tension) = $P \div v = 36000 \div 9 = 4000$ N = 4 kN

4 The dam at a certain hydroelectric power station is 170 m deep. The electrical power output from the generators at the base of the dam is 2000 MW. Given that 1 m^3 water has a mass of 1000 kg, calculate the minimum rate at which water leaves the dam in m^3 s^{-1} when electrical generation takes place at this rate. Why is this figure the **minimum** rate of flow? Take g as 9.81 m s^{-2}.

   Solution

   In 1 s, the potential energy converted to electrical energy is 2×10^3 MJ = 2×10^9 J
   Gravitational $p.e. = mgh = m \times 9.81 \times 170 = 1667.7 \times m$
   So mass removed from dam **every second** = $(2 \times 10^9) \div 1667.7 \approx 1.20 \times 10^6$ kg
   So rate of flow = $(1.2 \times 10^6) \div 1000 = 1200$ m^3 s^{-1}
   Calculated flow rate is a **minimum** because it has been assumed that all the gravitational potential energy has been converted into electrical energy and no allowance has been made for the wasted heat and sound energy.

Efficiency

Efficiency is a way of describing how good a device is at transferring energy from one form to another in an intended way.

If a light bulb is rated 100 W, this means that it normally uses 100 J of electrical energy every second. But it might only produce 5 J of light energy every second. The other 95 J are wasted as heat. This means that only 5% of the energy is transferred from electrical energy into light energy. This light bulb therefore has an efficiency of 0.05 or 5%. If the same light bulb were used as a heater, its efficiency would be 95% or 0.95, because the intended output energy form would be heat, not light.

Below are two equivalent equations which can be used to define efficiency. Since efficiency is a ratio of two quantities, each with the same unit, efficiency itself is dimensionless, that is, **efficiency has no unit**.

$$\text{efficiency} = \frac{\text{useful power output}}{\text{total power input}} \qquad \text{efficiency} = \frac{\text{useful energy output in a given time}}{\text{total energy input in the same time}}$$

Worked Examples

1 A filament lamp rated 60 W has an efficiency of 0.04 (4%). A modern long-life lamp is rated 12 W and produces the same useful output power as the filament lamp. Calculate (a) the useful output power of the filament lamp and (b) the efficiency of the long-life lamp.

   Solution

   (a) useful output power = efficiency × total input power = 0.04 × 60 = 2.4 W

   (b) $\text{efficiency} = \dfrac{\text{useful power output}}{\text{total power input}} = \dfrac{2.4}{12} = 0.2 = 20\%$

2 A wheel-and-axle is a simple machine in which a small effort force can be used to raise a heavy load. In the wheel-and-axle shown in the diagram on the right, a rope under 200 N tension (the effort) is wrapped around a 'wheel' of radius 20 cm to raise a load of weight 600 N.

   Calculate the machine's efficiency.

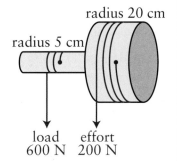

radius 20 cm
radius 5 cm
load 600 N   effort 200 N

   Solution

   When the wheel rotates once, the effort falls a distance of $(2 \times \pi \times 0.2)$ metres and at the same time the load rises through a distance of $(2 \times \pi \times 0.05)$ metres.

   For every revolution, the work done by the effort = $Fs = 200 \times (2 \times \pi \times 0.2) = 80\pi$ joules and the work done on the load = $Fs = 600 \times (2 \times \pi \times 0.05) = 60\pi$ joules

   $$\text{efficiency} = \frac{\text{useful energy output in a given time}}{\text{total energy input in the same time}} = \frac{60\pi}{80\pi} = 0.75 = 75\%$$

Energy conservation and energy efficiency

Modern life depends heavily on energy. We use energy every day to cook food, to wash, to keep warm, to remain cool (air conditioning), to light our homes and to power our electronic devices.

Energy conservation

> Note: Energy conservation should not be confused with the Principle of Conservation of Energy.

Energy conservation is defined as the act of reducing energy consumption. It is the act of minimising the wasteful use of energy resources in order to reduce the amount of energy consumed by society. This includes energy used to warm things, light things or move things.

Energy conservation has environmental benefits. Most of our energy resources are finite, such as fossil fuels (coal, oil and natural gas), and will eventually be exhausted. The burning of fossil fuels also releases large amounts of carbon dioxide into the atmosphere. Carbon dioxide is one of the largest contributors to the greenhouse effect, which raises the temperature of the Earth's surface and causes global warming. Taking steps to reduce the consumption of natural energy sources such as fossil fuels, biomass and fission fuels (uranium) will, in turn, reduce the amount of pollution they produce.

Energy efficiency

Energy efficiency is defined as any product or process that makes it possible to enjoy the same standard of living while using less energy. This is an important way of reducing the strain that energy production puts on the Earth's natural resources. There are many ways that we can save energy and improve our energy efficiency, such as:

- Turning down both the central heating and hot water thermostats – Turning them down by just 1 degree can reduce energy consumption by over 5%.
- Taking a shower – This uses about half the energy of taking a bath.
- Washing and drying clothes economically – Washing at a low temperature and ensuring that the washing machine has a full load will maximise the number of clothes washed for the energy consumed. Tumble dryers use a lot of energy, so drying clothes on a washing line or a 'clothes horse' also saves energy.
- Insulating homes – Almost one third of home heating escapes through the roof. This can be reduced by insulating the roof space with mineral wool or polystyrene. All houses built in recent years have polystyrene between the two layers of brick in the walls, but this may not be the case with older homes, where cavity wall insulation can be used to reduce heat loss.
- Turning off lights and appliances when not in use – Switching off lights when leaving the room and turning off electronic devices when not in use, rather than leaving them on standby, both reduce energy consumption.
- Using energy efficient appliances – Energy consumption can be reduced by using devices that are more efficient, i.e. those that convert more of the input energy into the desired output energy, such as LED light bulbs.

Exercise 1.8

Where relevant take g as 9.81 m s^{-2} and give your answer to an appropriate number of significant figures.

1 To enable a train to travel at a steady speed of 30 m s^{-1} along a level track, the engine must supply a pulling force of 50 kN.

   (a) How much work is the engine doing every second?

   (b) If the power is proportional to the cube of the velocity, how much power is needed to drive the train at a speed of 40 m s^{-1}?

2 A car mass 1500 kg increases its speed from 5 m s^{-1} to 15 m s^{-1} while moving 500 m up a constant slope. The gradient of the hill is sin $\alpha = \dfrac{1}{15}$.
   There is a constant resistance to motion of 250 N.
   Calculate:

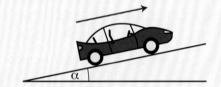

   (a) the increase in kinetic energy and potential energy.

   (b) the constant driving force exerted by the engine.

3 A lorry of mass 35 000 kg moves at a constant maximum speed, v, up an inclined road which rises 1.00 m for every 10.0 m travelled along the road. The output power of the engine is 175 kW. Calculate:

   (a) the value of v, if friction forces can be ignored.

   (b) the value of v, if the friction force is 4665 N.

4 A simple pendulum has a length of 1.00 m. The bob is pulled to one side so that the angle between the taut string and the vertical is 60.0°. The pendulum is then released.

   (a) Why can Newton's equations of motion not be applied in this situation?

   (b) Show that the maximum speed of the pendulum in its motion is 3.13 m s^{-1}.

5 Several stones are projected upwards with the same initial speed, u, but at different angles α ($\alpha > 0$) to the horizontal.

   (a) A student claims that at any common height reached by all of the stones, the *speed* of each stone is the same. Is the student right?

   (b) A stone is projected at 15.0 m s^{-1} at an unknown angle α ($\alpha > 0$) to the horizontal. Show that when it is 2.00 m above the ground the stone's speed is 13.6 m s^{-1}.

6 (a) Distinguish between kinetic energy and potential energy.

   (b) An object of mass 5 kg is allowed to roll down a slope from a vertical height of 15 m. It loses 30% of its energy when it reaches the bottom. Calculate the speed of the object when it reaches the bottom of the slope.

1.9 Electric Current, Charge, Potential Difference and Electromotive Force

Students should be able to:

1.9.1 Recall and use the equation $I = \dfrac{Q}{t}$

1.9.2 Recall and use the equations $V = \dfrac{W}{q}$, $V = \dfrac{P}{I}$

1.9.3 Define the volt

1.9.4 Define the electromotive force E

1.9.5 Distinguish between electromotive force and potential difference

Conduction in solids

Materials exhibit a very wide range of electrical conductivities. The best conductors, such as silver and copper, are over 10^{23} times better than the worst conductors, such as polythene. Between these extreme cases are materials known as semiconductors of which the most important are germanium and silicon.

The first requirement for conduction is a supply of charge carriers that can wander freely through the material. In solid, metallic conductors, the carriers are loosely-held outer electrons. With copper, for example, every atom contributes, on average, one 'free' electron which is not attached to any particular atom and so can participate in conduction. On the other hand, if all electrons in a material are required to form the bonds (covalent or ionic) that bind the atoms of the material together, then the material will be an insulator. In semiconductors only a small proportion of the charge carriers are 'free' to move throughout the lattice.

The 'free' electrons in a solid conductor are in a state of rapid motion, moving within the crystal lattice at speeds which depend on the lattice temperature. At room temperature, typical thermal speeds are around 1×10^{6} m s^{-1}. This motion is normally completely random, like that of gas molecules in the air. This means that as many electrons with a given speed move in one direction as in the opposite direction, as shown in the diagram on the right. Since the free electron motion is entirely random, we do not observe an electric current in such a material.

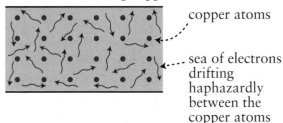

metallic conductor, eg copper

copper atoms

sea of electrons drifting haphazardly between the copper atoms

With no applied p.d., there is no net flow of charge and so no current flows.

However, when a battery is applied across the ends of a conductor, an electric field is created causing the electrons to accelerate towards the region of positive potential and to gain kinetic energy. This is shown in the diagram on the next page. Collisions between these accelerating electrons and the vibrating atoms in the crystal lattice cause the electrons to slow down and give up some of their kinetic energy to the atoms themselves. The effect is to transfer some of the chemical energy from the battery to the internal energy of the vibrating atoms in the lattice. This causes the atoms to vibrate more rapidly about their mean positions. Externally, we observe this increased internal energy as a temperature rise in the conductor. Electrical resistance is explained by collisions between the 'free electrons' and the vibrating atoms in the crystal lattice of the metal.

metallic conductor with a p.d. applied across it

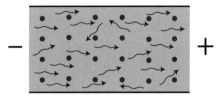

When a p.d. is applied, there is a net drift of electrons towards the region of higher potential.

Following any collision, the electrons accelerate once again and the process continues. The overall acceleration of the electrons is zero on account of these frequent collisions. However, there is a **drift of negative charge** towards the region of positive potential. **It is this drift of electrical charge which constitutes an electric current in a metal.** A typical drift velocity, for currents you might experience in an AS course, is less than 1 mm s^{-1}.

Current and charge

You will be aware from GCSE of the convention that current flows from the region of positive potential to that of negative or zero potential. However, in normal circumstances, the current, I, in metals is entirely due to the motion of electrons in the opposite direction to that of the conventional current. The quantity of electric charge flowing past a fixed point is defined in terms of the current. Thus, for a constant current I flowing for a time t we can write:

$$Q = It \quad \text{or} \quad I = \frac{Q}{t}$$

where Q = charge flowing past a fixed point, in coulombs
I = constant current in Amperes
t = time taken for charge to flow past fixed point in seconds

This tells us that a current of 1 A flowing in a circuit is equal to a charge of 1 C passing a fixed point in the circuit every second.

Worked example

1 If the charge on a single electron is -1.6×10^{-19} C, how many electrons flow past a fixed point every minute when a current of 2 A is flowing?

Solution

$Q = It = 2 \times 60 = 120$ C

Number of electrons = (Total Charge) ÷ (Charge on a single electron)

$= 120 \div 1.6 \times 10^{-19}$

$= 7.5 \times 10^{20}$ electrons

The fact that electrons have a negative charge has no bearing on this calculation.

Exercise 1.9A

1 What steady current flows when a charge of 300 mC flows past a fixed point in 5 seconds?

2 When there is a certain current in a wire, 6.0×10^{18} electrons pass a point in the wire in 1 second. Calculate the current flowing in the wire.

3 (a) When dealing with electric circuits the terms 'conventional current' and 'electron flow' are used. Explain the difference between these two terms.

   (b) A wire carries a current of 200 µA. How many charge carriers pass a point in the wire in 1 second?

4 A certain wire carries a current. In 5 seconds a total charge of 3.0 coulombs passes along the wire.

   (a) Calculate the current flowing in the wire.

   (b) How many charge carriers pass a point in the wire each second?

Electromotive force

Batteries and generators are able to maintain one terminal positive (i.e. deficient in electrons) and the other negative (i.e. with an excess of electrons). We can picture a battery as a pump which moves electrons from the negative terminal to the positive terminal around a circuit. **A battery therefore does work on charges and so energy must be changed within it.**

The work done is a measure of this energy transfer. When current flows in the filament of a torch bulb, for example, this stored chemical energy in the battery is first converted into electrical energy in the circuit, which in turn is changed into heat and light energy in the bulb.

A battery or generator is said to produce an electromotive force (e.m.f.), defined in terms of energy change.

The electromotive force (e.m.f.) of a battery is defined as the energy converted into electrical energy when unit charge (1 C) passes through it.

e.m.f. = electrical energy converted ÷ electric charge moved

$E = W \div Q$ where E = e.m.f. in volts
                            W = electric energy converted in joules
                            Q = charge in coulombs

The unit of e.m.f., like the unit of potential difference, is the volt.

The volt can be defined as a joule per coulomb (or, as we shall see later, a watt per ampere.)

> Remember:
>
> The potential difference between two points is the energy generated for every coulomb passing between them.
>
> The potential difference between two points is 1 volt if, when 1 coulomb passes between them, 1 joule of energy is generated.

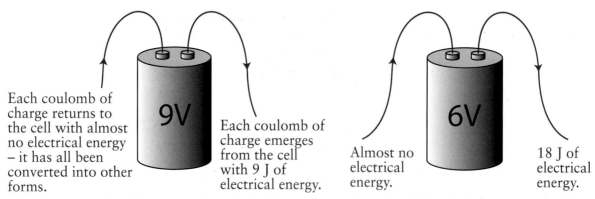

Each coulomb of charge returns to the cell with almost no electrical energy – it has all been converted into other forms.

Each coulomb of charge emerges from the cell with 9 J of electrical energy.

1 C of charge carries 9 J of energy away from a 9 V battery.

Almost no electrical energy.

18 J of electrical energy.

3 C of charge carries 18 J of energy away from a 6 V battery.

A car battery with an e.m.f. of 12 volts supplies 12 joules for every coulomb that passes through it; a power station generator with an e.m.f. of 25 000 volts is a much greater source of energy and supplies 25 000 joules per coulomb, 2 coulombs would receive 50 000 joules and so on.

In general, if a charge Q (in coulombs) passes through a source of e.m.f., E (in volts), the electrical energy supplied by the source W (in joules) is given by:

$W = QE$

Potential difference (p.d.)

It should be noted that although electromotive force (e.m.f.) and potential difference (p.d.) have the same unit, they deal with different aspects of an electric circuit. **Electromotive force applies to a source supplying electrical energy.** Potential difference refers to the conversion of electrical energy by a device **in a circuit.**

The term 'e.m.f.' is misleading to some extent, since it measures **energy per unit charge** and not force. It is true, however, that the source of e.m.f. is responsible for moving charges round the circuit. A voltmeter measures p.d. and one connected across the terminals of an electrical supply, such as a battery, records what is called the **terminal p.d.** of the battery.

If the battery is not connected to an external circuit and the voltmeter has a very high resistance, then the current through the battery will be negligible. We can regard the voltmeter as measuring the number of joules of electrical energy the battery supplies per coulomb, i.e. its e.m.f. Some people will therefore prefer to think of the e.m.f. of a battery as **the p.d. across its terminals** *on open circuit,* **that is, when no current is drawn from it.**

Our definition of the volt allows us to write:

$W = QV$ where W = work done or energy transformed in joules
Q = charge moved in coulombs
V = potential difference in volts

All sources of e.m.f. have an **internal resistance** from which the source cannot be separated. When the source provides an electrical current to some external load resistor, a voltage is also developed across this internal resistance. The difference between the e.m.f., E, and the voltage across the external load resistor, V, is equal to the voltage lost in the internal resistor. We will look in more detail at the internal resistance of a source of e.m.f. in section 1.11.

Electrical power

Electrical power is defined as the rate at which electrical energy is converted into other forms of energy by a circuit or a component, such as a resistor, in a circuit.

Electrical power, like mechanical power, is measured in watts (W).

If we divide both sides of the equation $W = QV$ by time, t, we arrive at:

$$\frac{W}{t} = \frac{QV}{t} = \frac{Q}{t} \times V = IV$$

And since work ÷ time is equal to power, we can write:

$P = IV$ where P = power in watts
I = current in amperes
V = potential difference in volts

Re-arranging this gives $V = \frac{P}{I}$, so the volt can also be thought of as **watts per ampere**.

Worked Examples

1 A battery of negligible internal resistance and e.m.f. 12 V is connected to a lamp marked 12 V, 24 W.

(a) What current flows through the lamp in normal use?

(b) How much electrical energy is used when this lamp is left on for 1 hour?

Solution

(a) Current = power ÷ current = 24 ÷ 12 = 2 A

(b) Power = 24 W = 24 J s^{-1}
Energy (in J) = power (in W) × time (in s) = 24 × 360 = 86 400 J

2 An electron in a cathode ray tube is accelerated from rest through a potential difference of 150 kV.

(a) Calculate the kinetic energy of the electrons when they collide with the screen.

(b) If the current in the tube is 32 mA, how many electrons strike the screen per second?

(c) At what rate must heat be dissipated from the screen when it reaches its working temperature?

Solution

(a) $W = QV = 1.6 \times 10^{-19} \times 150 \times 10^{3} = 2.4 \times 10^{-14}$ J

(b) From the definition of charge, the total charge arriving per second = 3.2 mC
Since the charge on each electron is (−) 1.6×10^{-19} C, the number of electrons arriving per second = $(3.2 \times 10^{-3}) \div (1.6 \times 10^{-19}) = 2 \times 10^{16}$ electrons.

(c) $P = IV = 3.2 \times 10^{-3} \times 150 \times 10^3 = 480$ W

3 A fully charged 12 V battery can deliver 1 A for 20 hours before it becomes flat. Calculate for the fully charged battery the total charge stored and the total energy stored.

Solution

Charge $Q = It = 1 \times 20 \times 3600 = 72\,000$ C $= 72$ kC

Energy $= QV = 72\,000 \times 12 = 864\,000$ J $= 864$ kJ

Exercise 1.9B

1 Define the electromotive force (e.m.f.) of a battery.

2 A battery has an e.m.f. of 12 V. Calculate how much energy is converted into electrical energy when a current of 50 mA passes for 100 s.

3 A battery has an e.m.f. of 9 V. Calculate how much energy is converted into electrical energy when the following charges pass through it:

(a) 1 C

(b) 15 µC

(c) A current of 500 mA for 12 s

4 A current of 50 mA passes through a resistor in 2 minutes and 24 J of energy are transferred through the resistor in this time. Calculate the potential difference across the resistor.

1.10 Resistance and Resistivity

Current-voltage relationship

The ammeter-voltmeter circuit shown on the right allows us to vary and measure the p.d. (voltage) V across a bulb and measure the corresponding current, I. This is known as the **two meter method**. By removing the bulb and replacing it with another component, such as a length of wire or a thermistor, the circuit can be used to obtain voltage and current measurements for that component.

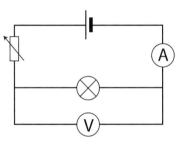

A graph of I against V showing the relationship between these two quantities is called the **characteristic** of the component. It summarises pictorially how the component behaves.

At GCSE level you may have come across graphs with voltage V on the y-axis and current I on the x-axis. For A level and beyond the practice is to show the relationship as a graph of **voltage on the x-axis** and **current on the y-axis**. An example of the **characteristic** for a metallic conductor at constant temperature is shown on the right. Observe that the **graph passes through two quadrants**. So when a voltage of opposite polarity is applied, the current flow is in the reverse direction.

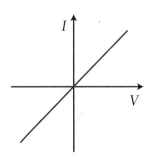

I–V characteristic curve for a metallic conductor

Ohm's Law

Ohm's Law states that the current through a metallic conductor is directly proportional to the applied p.d., *provided the temperature is constant.*

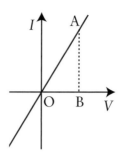

Materials that obey Ohm's Law are called **ohmic** conductors. A graph of current against voltage for an ohmic conductor is a straight line, as shown on the right.

Since *I* is directly proportional to *V* it follows that $\frac{V}{I}$ = a constant.

This constant is equal to the **reciprocal** of the gradient, i.e. by OB ÷ AB.

The ratio $\frac{V}{I}$ is called the **resistance**, *R*, of a conductor and is measured in **ohms** (Ω).

Resistance is calculated using the formula:

$$R = \frac{V}{I}$$

where *R* = resistance in ohms
V = potential difference in volts
I = current in amperes

You will recall from the definition of potential difference, *V*, in section 1.10, that we were able to write the familiar equation for electrical power, *P = IV*. We can combine this equation with that for Ohm's Law.

Since: $\qquad\qquad\qquad P = IV$ and $V = IR$

then substituting for *V* gives: $\quad P = I^2R$

and substituting for *I* gives: $\quad P = \dfrac{V^2}{R}$

We therefore arrive at the set of equations below. Collectively, these equations are referred to as **Joule's Law** of electrical heating.

$$P = IV = I^2R = \frac{V^2}{R}$$

Note: You need to memorise these equations.

Worked Examples

1 A train of mass 100 000 kg operates from a 25 kV supply and can accelerate to a speed of 20 m s^{-1} in 50 seconds along a level stretch of track. Calculate the average current it uses, assuming no energy losses.

Solution

Average mechanical power = *k.e.* ÷ time = ½ × 100 000 × 20^2 ÷ 50 = 400 000 W

$I = \dfrac{P}{V}$ = 400 000 ÷ 25 000 = 16 A

2 A consumer requires to use 5 kW at a p.d. of 240 V which is connected to a distant generator by leads which have a total resistance of 2.0 Ω. Calculate the current flowing in the leads and the p.d. across the leads at the generator.

Solution

Current $I = \dfrac{P}{V}$ = 5000 ÷ 240 = 20.83 A

Voltage lost in resistance of leads = IR = 20.83 × 2 = 41.66 V

Voltage at generator = 41.66 + 240 = 281.66 V

3 An electric boiler is rated 2645 W and has a heating element of resistance 20 Ω. Calculate the resistance of its heating element.

Solution

$P = I^2R$, so 2645 = I^2 × 20

Thus $I = \sqrt{(2645 \div 20)} = \sqrt{(132.25)}$ = 11.5 A

Ohmic and non-Ohmic behaviour

As we have seen, when the current flowing through a material is directly proportional to the p.d. across it, that material is said to be **ohmic**. Copper wire at constant temperature is an example of an ohmic material.

If the temperature is allowed to rise with increasing current, as occurs in the filament of a lamp, then the *I–V* characteristic curve is as shown on the right. This means that with increasing current (and hence increasing temperature) the resistance of a metal wire increases. However, as the temperature is increasing, the conditions pertaining to Ohm's Law are not constant, so we call this **non-Ohmic** behaviour. We will return later to explain the reasons for this increasing resistance.

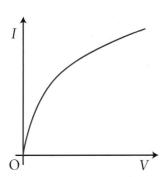

I–V characteristic curve for a filament lamp

Diode

A diode is a semiconductor device which has low (ideally zero) resistance to current in one direction and high (ideally infinite) resistance in the other. The most common diode consists of a junction of two types of semiconductor (p type and n type). The image to the right shows a diode and the circuit symbol.

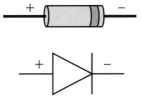

The *I–V* characteristic curve on the right shows that this diode does not conduct well until the voltage applied exceeds 0.6 V. Beyond this voltage the resistance of the diode is very small. Remember, the resistance for this type of graph is the **reciprocal** of the gradient.

When a diode is connected to the terminals of a voltage supply, with the positive and negative at the ends shown on the circuit symbol, the diode is said to be **forward biased.**

When the diode connections are reversed, so that the end that was previously positive is now connected to the negative terminal of the voltage supply, it is said to be **reverse biased.** If the diode is reversed in the circuit it conducts poorly. The current remains small as the voltage is increased.

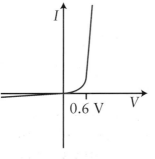

I–V characteristic curve for a diode

Thermistors

Thermistors are made of semiconductor materials such as silicon or germanium. The circuit symbol for a thermistor is shown below. The AS course requires knowledge of a type of thermistor called a negative temperature coefficient (ntc) thermistor. The resistance of an ntc thermistor decreases as it heats up, for reasons that are discussed below. The *I–V* characteristic curve for an ntc thermistor is shown on the right.

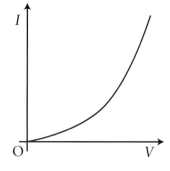

I–V characteristic curve for an ntc thermistor

Experiment: How the resistance of an ntc thermistor varies with temperature

Set up the circuit as shown on the right. Pour hot water into the beaker so that the thermistor is covered. Record the temperature, voltage and current as the water cools. Calculate the resistance of the thermistor at the various temperatures and plot a graph.

The graph below (left) shows a resistance-temperature graph for an ntc thermistor. The resistance decreases as the temperature increases. This is an exponential decrease.

By comparison, the resistance of a metal rises linearly with temperature as shown in the graph below (right). Although there is a linear relationship, **the resistance is not directly proportional to the temperature.** The straight line graph does not pass through the origin, because at 0°C the metal still has resistance.

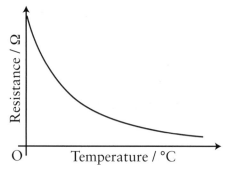

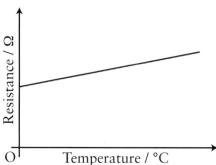

Why do metals and thermistors behave so differently?

When the temperature of a metal increases, the atoms vibrate with greater amplitude and much more violently than before. This causes the free electrons to collide more frequently and with greater force with the atoms in the lattice. These more frequent collisions reduce the average drift speed of the electrons and hence increase the time they take to move between two fixed points in the circuit. This in turn means that, for a given p.d., the current is reduced. Hence the resistance of the metal **increases.**

With thermistors two effects are taking place simultaneously. The increase in temperature would tend to increase the free electron-atom collision frequency and hence increase the resistance, as occurs with metals. However, only a small amount of energy binds the electrons to the thermistor's atoms within the lattice. With rising temperature, the lattice atoms vibrate with increasing amplitude. If the vibration is sufficiently violent, many, many electrons break free. There is such an enormous increase in the number of free electron charge carriers that there is a huge **increase** in the current for a given voltage. Since $R = V \div I$, this results in a reduction in the thermistor's resistance. Of the two effects, the increase in the number of free charge carriers (which would tend to decrease resistance) and the decrease in the electrons' average drift speed (which would tend to increase resistance), the former is by far the **greater**. The consequence is a net **reduction** in the resistance of the thermistor.

The name **negative temperature coefficient thermistor** is used because of the fact that resistance generally falls as the temperature rises.

Thermistors can be used as thermometers, and as part of electronic circuits which are switched on and off automatically by a change in temperature.

Current, voltage and resistance in series and parallel circuits

The ammeter-voltmeter circuit (the two-meter method) can be used to investigate the relationship between the voltage, current and resistance of resistors in series and parallel circuits. The circuits are shown below.

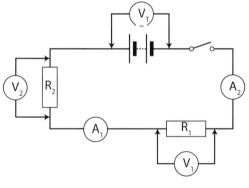

Series circuit

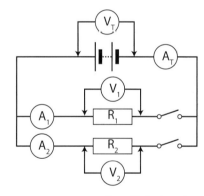

Parallel circuit

A voltmeter is connected in parallel with the resistors and a battery or power supply, and is used to measure the voltage, V, across each of the components. To measure the current, I, an ammeter is placed in series with the resistors. This requires breaking the circuit at those points, inserting the ammeter and reconnecting the circuit.

Once measurements of the voltage and current have been taken, the resistance can then be calculated as the ratio of the voltage and current, i.e. $R = \dfrac{V}{I}$.

Resistors in series

The current is the same everywhere in a series circuit. The supply voltage is equal to the sum of the voltages across each of the series components. We can demonstrate mathematically how this leads to the **series resistance formula**:

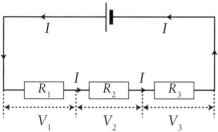

Consider the circuit shown on the right. What single resistor R_T could replace these three resistors yet allow the same current I to pass for the same total p.d.?

Total Resistance, R_T = (total p.d.) ÷ (current)

$$= (V_1 + V_2 + V_3) \div I$$

$$R_T = V_1 \div I + V_2 \div I + V_3 \div I$$

$$R_T = R_1 + R_2 + R_3$$

Resistors in parallel

When resistors are in parallel the p.d. across each resistor is the same. The sum of the currents through each resistor is equal to the total current taken from the supply. We can demonstrate mathematically how this leads to the **parallel resistance formula**:

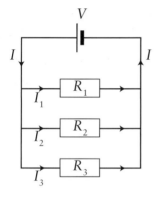

Consider the circuit shown on the right. What single resistor R_T could replace these three resistors yet allow the same current I to pass for the same total p.d.?

Total Resistance, $R_T = V \div I$ and since $R_1 = V \div I_1$,

$R_2 = V \div R_2$ and $R_3 = V \div I_3$ and $I = I_1 + I_2 + I_3$

Then, $I = V \div R_1 + V \div R_2 + V \div R_3$ so,

$$I = \frac{V}{R_T} = \frac{V}{R_1} + \frac{V}{R_2} + \frac{V}{R_3}$$

Dividing by V gives: $\dfrac{1}{R_T} = \dfrac{1}{R_1} + \dfrac{1}{R_2} + \dfrac{1}{R_3}$

When there are **just two resistors** the equation $\dfrac{1}{R_T} = \dfrac{1}{R_1} + \dfrac{1}{R_2}$ reduces to:

$$R_T = \frac{R_1 \times R_2}{R_1 + R_2}$$

This is often easier to use, but it must be applied repeatedly when there are three or more resistors.

It is important to remember that:

- the **total resistance** of any **series** arrangement is always **greater than the largest resistance** in that network.

- the **total resistance** of any **parallel** arrangement is always **less than the smallest resistance** in the parallel network.

- the **total resistance** of *N* **equal resistors** *R* arranged in parallel is simply *R* ÷ *N*.

You may recall using the last point at GCSE to calculate the resistance of two, equal parallel resistors as the half of one of them.

Hybrid circuits

Hybrid circuits consist of a mixture of parallel and series elements, such as the one shown on the right. Here a heating element of resistance 3 Ω is placed in parallel with a series arrangement of two other heaters of resistance 2 Ω and 4 Ω. How could we find the total resistance of the combination?

Applying the series equation first gives the resistance of the 2 Ω and 4 Ω combination as 6 Ω.

Now applying the equation for parallel networks:

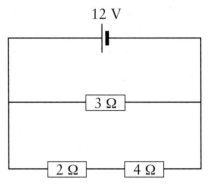

$$\frac{1}{R_T} = \frac{1}{R_1} + \frac{1}{R_2} = \frac{1}{6} + \frac{1}{3} = \frac{1}{2}$$

Hence, $R_T = 2\ \Omega$.

We can also deduce the current and voltage in or across each component. The voltage across the 3 Ω resistor = the voltage across the 2 Ω + 4 Ω combination = 12 V.

The current in each of the series elements is given by $I = V \div R = 12 \div 6 = 2$ A.

The current in the 3 Ω resistor is similarly $12 \div 3 = 4$ A.

So the current drawn from the battery, $I_b = V_b \div R_T = 12 \div 2 = 6$ A, which is equal to the sum of the currents in the parallel branches of the circuit (2 A + 4 A).

Resistivity

The resistance of a metal conductor at a constant temperature depends on:

- its length, l
- its area of cross-section, A
- the material from which it is made.

Length

The resistance of a metal wire is **directly proportional** to its length. So, if the length of wire is doubled, the resistance also doubles. This is shown in the graph on the right.

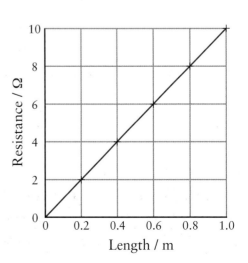

Area of cross-section

As the area of cross-section increases, the resistance of the wire decreases. This is shown by the graph on the right. In fact the resistance of the wire is **inversely proportional** to the area of cross-section. This means as the area of cross-section is doubled then the resistance is halved. Mathematically, the curve shown by the graph is called a hyperbola and it follows the equation:

$RA = k$ where R = resistance
          A = cross-section area
          k = a constant

In this case, RA is approximately equal to 0.15 Ωm^2.

How else might we show this graphically? Is it possible to obtain a straight line graph? From the equation above, we see that:

$R = k(\dfrac{1}{A})$ where k is a constant

So we need to plot a graph of resistance against 1 / area of cross-section, as shown on the right.

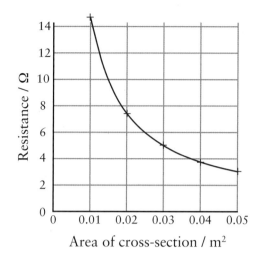

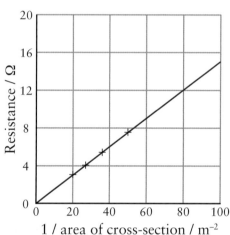

Material

The resistance also depends on the material of the conductor. A piece of copper with the identical dimensions to a piece of steel will have a very different resistance.

Each material has a constant known as its **resistivity** and is given the symbol ρ (pronounced 'rho'). If we combine all these ideas, we have:

$R = \dfrac{\rho l}{A}$ where R = Resistance in Ω
          A = area of cross-section in m^2
          l = length in m
          ρ = resistivity in Ωm

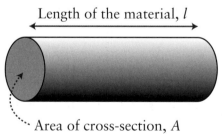

Re-arranging this to give $\rho = \dfrac{RA}{l}$ provides us with a definition of resistivity.

The resistivity of a material is defined as numerically equal to the resistance of a sample of the material 1 m long and of cross-sectional area 1 m^2.

The resistivities of materials vary widely, as shown in the table on the next page.

Type of substance	Material	Resistivity in Ωm	Use
Metals	Silver	1.8×10^{-8}	Switch contacts
	Copper	1.7×10^{-8}	Connecting cables
	Aluminium	2.9×10^{-8}	Power cables
	Tungsten	5.5×10^{-8}	Lamp filaments
Alloys	Manganin	44×10^{-8}	Standard resistors
	Eureka	49×10^{-8}	Variable resistors
	Nichrome	110×10^{-8}	Heating elements
Non-Metal	Carbon (graphite)	185×10^{-8}	Radio resistors
Semiconductors	Germanium	0.6	Transistors
	Silicon	2300	Transistors
Insulators	Glass	10^{10} to 10^{14}	
	Polystyrene	10^{15}	

Note: While there is no requirement to know any of the details in the above table, you should be able to recall that metals have resistivity of around 1×10^{-8} Ωm, while good insulators have resistivity of around 1×10^{15} Ωm.

Measuring resistivity experimentally

This is an experiment which is prescribed within the specification. It is important that you do the experiment as part of your training in practical classes and that you can give a detailed description of the procedure for the theory examination. The resistance wire under investigation, which has been previously freed from bends and kinks, is laid along a metre stick and secured in position at each end by means of insulating tape. The electrical circuit is then set up as shown in the diagram on the right. Connections to the resistance wire are usually made using crocodile clips.

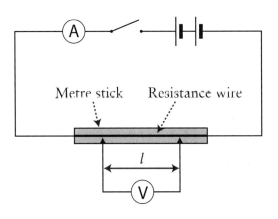

The experiment involves measuring the voltage across different lengths of resistance wire and the current passing through for lengths l ranging from about 20 cm to about 90 cm. From the voltage, V, and current, I, the resistance, R, can be found using $R = V \div I$. This is done at least twice per length of resistance wire to reduce the possibility of random error. At this stage we should plot a graph of R against l. The graph will be a straight line through the origin. Now we find the gradient of this line to determine the resistance per metre length of wire ($R \div l$).

Using a micrometer screw gauge we now measure the diameter of the wire at about six points along its length. From this data we can determine the average diameter <d> and using $A = \pi<d>^2 \div 4$ we can find the wire's average cross-section area, A.

The last stage is to calculate the resistivity of the material of the wire, ρ. Since the resistivity is defined by the equation:

$$\rho = \frac{RA}{l} = \frac{R.\pi <d>^2}{4l} = \text{gradient of } R\text{-}l \text{ graph} \times \frac{\pi <d>^2}{4}$$

Worked Examples

1 What length of resistance wire must be cut from a reel if the material has resistivity 1.57×10^{-8} Ωm, diameter 0.18 mm and is required to have a resistance as close as possible to 2.50 Ω?

   Solution

   Rearranging $\rho = (R \div l)A$ gives $l = RA \div \rho = R\pi d^2 \div 4\rho$
        Hence $l = 2.50 \times \{\pi \times (0.18 \times 10^{-3})^2\} \div (4 \times 1.57 \times 10^{-8})$
            $l = 4.05$ m

2 An electric hot plate consists of a 20 m length of manganin wire of resistivity of 4.4×10^{-7} Ωm and cross-section area 0.23 mm². Calculate the power of the plate when connected to a 200 V electrical supply.

   Solution

   $P = IV = V^2 \div R = V^2 A \div \rho l$
        $= (200^2 \times 0.23 \times 10^{-6}) \div (4.4 \times 10^{-7} \times 20)$
        $= 1045$ W

3 A 960 Ω filament for an electric light bulb is made of 60 cm of tungsten wire of resistivity 5.5×10^{-8} Ωm. Calculate the diameter of the wire.

   Solution

   $A = l\rho \div R = (0.6 \times 5.5 \times 10^{-8}) \div 960$
      $= 3.4375 \times 10^{-11}$ m²

   $D = \sqrt{(4A \div \pi)}$
      $= \sqrt{\{(4 \times 3.4375 \times 10^{-11}) \div \pi\}}$
      $= 6.62 \times 10^{-6}$ m

Superconductivity

As we have seen, even metals – regarded as good conductors – have a measurable electrical resistance and this resistance decreases as the temperature falls. In 1908, a physicist called Kammerlingh Onnes succeeded in cooling helium to a temperature around –269°C, which corresponds to a temperature of around 4 Kelvin. This allowed the investigation of the electrical properties of metals at really low temperatures.

One of the first metals studied was mercury. Below –40°C mercury is a solid. What astonished Onnes was that at around 4 Kelvin the resistance of mercury fell to zero as

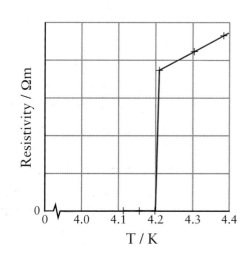

shown in the graph on the previous page. This was the first **superconductor**.

We can define a material as a superconductor if it loses all its electrical resistivity to become a perfect conductor when it is below its critical temperature.

Since the effect was discovered, many metallic alloys have been found which exhibit superconductivity and the search has been on for superconductors at room temperature (around 20°C or 293 Kelvin). At the moment the most promising materials are ceramic alloys, of which one is a superconductor at around –148°C (125 Kelvin), so there is still a long way to go.

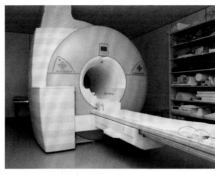

An MRI scanner

Superconductors are likely to be found in **very many applications** later this century. They are already used to produce the extremely strong magnetic fields needed for the **Magnetic Resonance Imaging (MRI) scanners** used in hospitals for diagnostic purposes. Here the major expense is the liquefied gases needed to keep the superconductor sufficiently cold.

Another application is **maglev (magnetic levitation) transport**. Here superconducting magnets are used to get vehicles (notably modern railway carriages) to float on strong superconducting magnets. This almost completely eliminates friction between the train and the track.

A Maglev train

In both applications a superconductor at room temperature would be a major technological breakthrough.

A third application is **the transmission of electrical power** – the need for huge transmission voltages would be all but eliminated if superconductors could be developed at 'ordinary' temperatures.

Exercise 1.10

1 (a) Define electrical resistivity.

   (b) A student plans to measure the resistivity of nichrome wire. They are given a length of the wire which is just over 1 m long.

      (i) Draw a labelled diagram of a circuit using the ammeter-voltmeter method, which could be used to measure the resistance of one such piece of wire.

      (ii) Describe how the quantities that are required to calculate the resistivity would be measured. Include experimental detail.

      (iii) What graph should be plotted? Describe how it is used to measure the resistivity of nichrome.

2 (a) A student writes *"The resistivity of the copper wire is $1.9 \times 10^{-7} \, \Omega \, m^{-1}$"*.

      The student's numerical values are correct, but two errors have been made in the statement. Identify the errors and show how they should be corrected.

(b) The resistivity of iron is 5 times that of copper. An iron wire of length L and diameter D has a resistance R. What length of copper wire of diameter ½D would also have a resistance R? Give your answer in terms of L, the length of the iron wire.

3 (a) Describe the difference between an ohmic conductor and a non-ohmic conductor.

(b) Sketch the $I–V$ graphs for a metal wire at constant temperature and a filament lamp. Label the axes on each graph and state if it is an example of ohmic or non-ohmic behaviour.

(c) Explain how each graph can be used to determine the resistance of the component.

4 Using the circuit shown on the right, the voltage and current for different lengths of the resistance wire were measured. The results are shown in the table below. The diameter of the wire was measured at a number of places and the results are shown below.

Diameter of the wire/mm:
0.32, 0.31, 0.33, 0.32, 0.31, 0.32

Length / m	Voltage / V	Current / A	Resistance / Ω
0.10	0.50	0.36	
0.20	0.90	0.33	
0.30	1.00	0.24	
0.40	1.20	0.22	
0.50	1.50	0.21	
0.60	1.70	0.20	
0.70	1.90	0.19	

Using the measurements shown above, determine the resistivity of the metal used in the resistance wire.

5 Sections of two circuits are shown below.

(a) Calculate the total resistance of Circuit 1 between A and B.

(b) An additional resistor is added as shown in Circuit 2. Calculate the total resistance between A and B when this additional resistor is added.

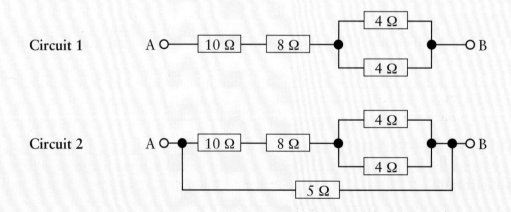

1.11 Internal Resistance and Electromotive Force

Students should be able to:

1.11.1 Demonstrate an understanding of the simple consequences of internal resistance of a source for external circuits

1.11.2 Use the equation $V = E - Ir$

1.11.3 Perform and describe an experiment to measure internal resistance and the electromotive force

Internal resistance

Sources of e.m.f. (electromotive force), such as batteries and power packs, have themselves some resistance to the electric current that passes through them. This is called their **internal** resistance.

The internal resistance of a source of e.m.f. has two effects:

1 As more current is drawn from the battery or power pack, the voltage across the terminals of the supply falls.

2 The source of e.m.f. is less than 100% efficient as energy is dissipated as heat within it.

The voltage stated on the label of a source of e.m.f. such as a battery is the voltage measured across its terminal when **no current** is being drawn from it. This is called the **open-circuit voltage**. The internal resistance of a source of e.m.f. may be thought of as a **resistance, r, in series with the supply**.

In the circuit on the right and in the discussion below:

E = e.m.f. of the cell
V = voltage across the terminals
r = internal resistance
R = load resistance
v = voltage lost in internal resistance

Total resistance = $R + r$

Current $I = \dfrac{E}{(R + r)}$

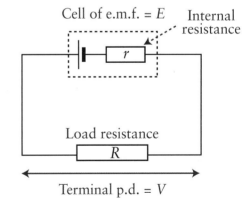

Cell of e.m.f. = E Internal resistance

Load resistance R

Terminal p.d. = V

The potential difference across the load resistance is known as the **terminal potential difference**, V, where $V = IR$.

The potential difference lost in the internal resistance is $v = Ir$, so:

$E = V + v = IR + Ir = I(R + r)$

The maximum current that can be taken from a power supply occurs when the cell is short-circuited (so there is no load resistance, $R = 0$) is:

$I_{max} = \dfrac{E}{R}$

Internal resistance and the Law of Conservation of Energy

Analysis of the circuit on the previous page shows that:

$E = V + Ir$

If both sides of the equation are multiplied by I, the result is:

$$EI \quad = \quad VI \quad + \quad I^2r$$

| Power released by chemical energy in the battery | Power delivered to the external circuit | Power dissipated in the internal resistance of the battery |

This is simply an application of the Law of Conservation of Energy to a battery with an internal resistance.

Worked examples

1 When the current drawn from a dry cell is 1 A, the voltage across the cell's terminals is 0.5 V. When the current drawn is 0.5 A, the terminal p.d. is 1 V. Calculate the e.m.f. of the cell and its internal resistance.

   Solution

   Using $E = I(R + r)$ and $R = V \div I$,

   Terminal p.d. = 0.5 V, I = 1 A, so $R = 0.5 \div 1 = 0.5\ \Omega$ and $E = 1(0.5 + r) = 0.5 + r$ [1]

   Terminal p.d. = 1.0 V, I = 0.5 A, so $R = 1 \div 0.5 = 2\ \Omega$ and $E = 0.5(2 + r) = 1 + 0.5r$ [2]

   Subtracting [2] from [1] gives $0 = -0.5 + 0.5r$

   Hence, $r = 1\ \Omega$ and $E = 1.5$ V

2 When a 12 V battery is short-circuited, the current drawn is 6 A. What current would you expect to flow when the load resistor is 4 Ω?

   Solution

   Internal resistance = $V \div I = 12 \div 6 = 2\ \Omega$

   When the load is 4 Ω, the total resistance is 2 + 4 = 6 Ω, and $I = 12 \div 6 = 2$ A

3 Three identical cells each have an internal resistance of 0.5 Ω. They are connected in series with each other across a load resistor of 1.5 Ω. If the e.m.f. of each cell is 2.0 V, calculate the current drawn from the battery and the power dissipated in the load resistor.

   Solution

   I = battery voltage ÷ circuit resistance = $(3 \times 2.0) \div (3 \times 0.5 + 1.5)$

   $= 6.0 \div 3.0$

   $= 2.0$ A

   Power in external resistor = $I^2R = 2.0^2 \times 1.5 = 6.0$ W

4 When a 2.5 Ω resistor is connected across a battery of e.m.f. 6.0 V, the terminal p.d. is 5.0 V.

(a) What resistor could be **added** to the circuit to reduce the total load resistance to 0.5 Ω and how should it be connected?

(b) What power does the battery deliver to the load when this resistance is added?

Solution

(a) Current = $V \div I$ = 5.0 ÷ 2.5 = 2.0 A

Total resistance = 6.0 ÷ 2.0 = 3.0 Ω, so internal resistance = 3.0 − 2.5 = 0.5 Ω

To obtain a total load resistance (0.5 Ω) **less** than the present external resistance (2.5 Ω), the extra resistor must be placed **in parallel with the 2.5 Ω.**

$$\frac{1}{R_{total}} = \frac{1}{R_1} + \frac{1}{R_2}$$

So, if R_{total} = 0.5 Ω, R_1 = 2.5 Ω and the required resistance is R_2, then

$$\frac{1}{0.5} = \frac{1}{2.5} + \frac{1}{R_2}$$

$$\frac{1}{R_2} = \frac{1}{0.5} - \frac{1}{2.5} = 1.6$$

So, additional resistance R_2 = 1 ÷ 1.6 = 0.625 Ω

(b) Total resistance = $R_{load} + R_{internal}$ = 0.5 + 0.5 = 1.0 Ω

Current from battery = $V \div I$ = 6.0 ÷ 1.0 = 6.0 A = current through load combination (0.5 Ω)

Power in load = I^2R = 6.0^2 × 0.5 = 18 W

Experiment to find the internal resistance of a cell

Determination of the internal resistance of a cell is an experiment prescribed by the specification. You should therefore have carried out the experiment in practical classes and be able to describe the procedure in detail.

Set up the circuit as shown on the right. The experiment involves recording values of the terminal voltage, V, and current drawn from the cell, I, for different load resistances, R. A 'D' cell (commonly called a torch battery) is suitable for the purpose. It is not necessary to know the values of the load resistance, but typically it should range from zero to about 5 Ω.

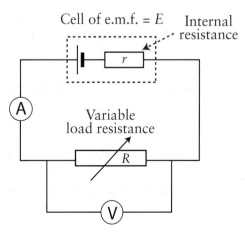

The results are interpreted as follows.

Since: $E = I(r + R) = Ir + IR$

Then: $E = Ir + V$

Rearranging gives: $V = E - Ir$

So a graph of V against I gives a straight line of gradient $-r$ and y-axis intercept of E, as shown in the diagram below.

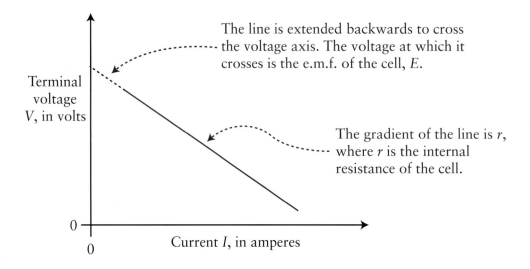

The line is extended backwards to cross the voltage axis. The voltage at which it crosses is the e.m.f. of the cell, E.

The gradient of the line is r, where r is the internal resistance of the cell.

Exercise 1.11

1 Explain the difference between electromotive force (e.m.f) and terminal potential difference.

2 A battery has an e.m.f. of 12 V. It supplies a current 1.8 A to a resistance of 6.0 Ω as shown below.

   (a) Calculate the internal resistance of the battery.

   (b) Another 6.0 Ω resistor is connected in parallel with the first one. Calculate the current drawn from the battery now.

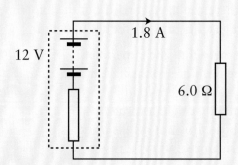

3 The variable resistor in the circuit shown on the right was adjusted and two sets of readings were taken as shown in the table below.

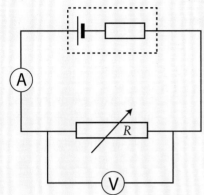

Voltmeter reading / V	Ammeter reading / A
6.0	2.0
7.2	1.2

Using these values find the e.m.f of the battery and its internal resistance.

4 Using the circuit shown on the right, values of the terminal voltage, V, and current drawn from the cell, I, were recorded for different load resistances, R. The results of this experiment are shown in the table below.

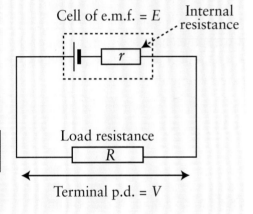

Terminal voltage / V	1.25	1.0	0.75	0.5	0.25
Current / A	0.25	0.5	0.75	1.0	1.25

Plot a graph using the data shown above and determine the internal resistance, r, and e.m.f., E, of the cell.

1.12 Potential Divider Circuits

Students should be able to:

1.12.1 Demonstrate an understanding of the use of a potential divider to supply variable potential difference from a fixed power supply

1.12.2 Demonstrate knowledge and understanding of the use of the potential divider in lighting and heating control circuits

1.12.3 Calculate the output voltages in loaded circuits using the equation

$$V_{OUT} = \frac{R_1 V_{IN}}{R_1 + R_2}$$

Potential divider

A potential divider is an arrangement of resistors which allows a fraction of the p.d. supplied to it to be passed on to an external circuit.

In the circuit shown on the right the current, I, in resistor R_1 is given by:

$$I = \frac{V_{IN}}{R_1 + R_2}$$

The output voltage is the potential difference across R_1, so:

$$V_{OUT} = IR_1 .$$

Applying Ohm's Law to R_1 gives:

$$V_{OUT} = \frac{R_1 V_{IN}}{R_1 + R_2}$$

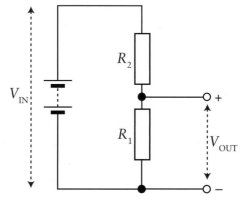

Potential divider with fixed resistors

The output voltage is generally applied across some external device known as the load. This type of potential divider is particularly useful where the power supply provides a greater voltage than that required by the load. However, **it does not permit the user to vary the voltage across the load.** To do that **the fixed resistors are replaced by a continuously variable resistor called a rheostat,** as shown in the diagram on the right. The output voltage is then continuously variable.

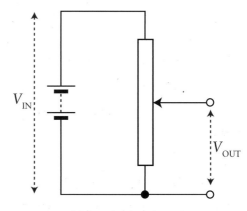

Potential divider with a rheostat

Worked example

1 A potential divider is set up as shown in the diagram on the right.

   (a) Calculate the potential difference between A and B.

   (b) A voltmeter of resistance 1000 Ω is connected across the terminals A and B. What is the reading on the voltmeter?

Solution

(a) $V_{AB} = \dfrac{R_1 V_{IN}}{R_1 + R_2} = 500 \times 6 \div (1000 + 500) = 4\text{ V}$

(b) Connecting the voltmeter in parallel with the 1000 Ω modifies the circuit. As the diagram on the right shows, it is equivalent to two 1000 Ω resistors in parallel, a total resistance of 500 Ω. So:

$V_{AB} = \dfrac{R_1 V_{IN}}{R_1 + R_2} = 500 \times 6 \div (500 + 500) = 3\text{ V}$

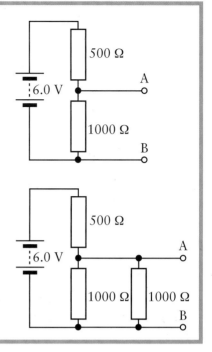

Effect of loading on V_{OUT}

In the example above, the addition of the 400 Ω across the terminals P and Q has reduced the maximum output voltage of the potential divider from 4.0 V to 2.4 V. In general, the voltage across the load decreases as the resistance of the load decreases. In the extreme case where there is infinite load resistance, V_{OUT} is a maximum. If there is zero load resistance, the potential divider is short-circuited and V_{OUT} is zero.

Engineers and circuit designers use a general rule-of-thumb, which states that the load resistance must always be greater than ten times the potential divider's resistance to ensure that there is no appreciable voltage drop caused by adding the external resistance (the load).

Potential divider in lighting circuits

If one of the resistors in a potential divider is replaced by a light dependent resistor (LDR), a circuit controlling lights can be constructed. A picture of an LDR and its circuit symbol are shown on the right. The resistance of an LDR changes with light illumination.

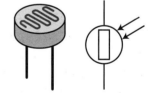

In the circuit on the right $R_2 = 10\text{ k}\Omega$ and R_1 is an LDR.

In the dark this LDR's resistance = 200 kΩ and in bright light its resistance is 0.5 kΩ.

The input voltage $V_{IN} = 9.0\text{ V}$

So in bright light $V_{OUT} = 0.5 \times 9 \div 10.5 = 0.43\text{ V}$

And in the dark $V_{OUT} = 200 \times 9 \div (200 + 10) = 8.57\text{ V}$

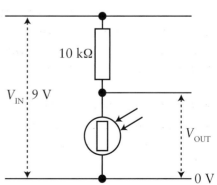

This circuit gives a low voltage output when the LDR is in bright light and a high voltage when it is in darkness. This high voltage output can then be used operate a control system that switches on lights.

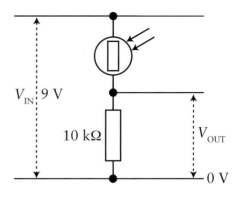

If the positions of the LDR and the fixed resistor are switched, as shown in the diagram on the right, then the output voltages are also reversed.

Now, the output voltage is high in bright light and low in darkness. You can check the value using the potential divider equation.

Potential divider in heating circuits

The resistance of a thermistor varies with temperature. In the case of an ntc thermistor the resistance decreases as the temperature increases.

In one particular ntc thermistor the resistance at 0°C is 70 kΩ and at 100°C it is 1 kΩ. It is connected to a circuit as shown in the diagram on the right. So:

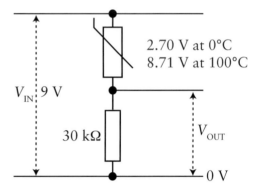

At 0°C $\quad V_{out} = 30 \times 9 \div (30 + 70) = 2.70$ V

At 100°C $V_{out} = 30 \times 9 \div (30 + 1) = 8.71$ V

This can be used as part of a fire alarm circuit. It produces a high voltage output when hot conditions are detected.

By contrast, a circuit that warns drivers when ice conditions are present needs to produce a high voltage at low temperatures. Reversing the positions of the fixed resistor and ntc thermistor produces such a circuit, as shown in the diagram on the right.

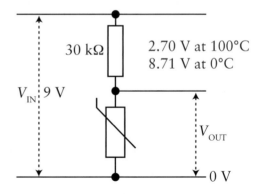

Thermistors used in potential dividers have a number of applications in cars, ranging from the ice warning system mentioned above to air conditioning and seat temperature controls.

Exercise 1.12

1 A potential divider circuit is shown on the right.

Calculate the potential difference between P and Q.

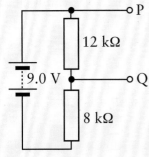

2 A light dependent resistor (LDR) is used in a potential divider circuit as shown on the right.

The input voltage V_{in} = 9 V.

The resistance of the LDR in bright light is 0.5 kΩ and in the dark it is 3.0 kΩ.

Calculate the maximum and minimum values of the output voltage V_{out}.

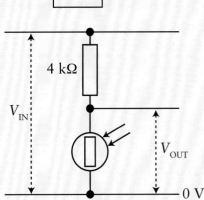

3 Provide a voltage supply, continuously variable from 0 to 6 V. A fixed 9 V supply, a rheostat (which may be used as a potential divider) of total resistance 10 kΩ and a selection of resistors are available.

(a) Draw a suitable circuit to provide this variable supply. Calculate the resistance of the additional resistor required. Label the components of your circuit with their values, and mark the polarities of the 9 V supply and the output terminals.

(b) A voltmeter of resistance 20 kΩ is connected across the output terminals and the rheostat is set at its mid-point value. Calculate the reading on the voltmeter.

4 A technician is asked to construct a potential divider circuit to deliver an output voltage of 1.2 V, using a battery of e.m.f. 3.0 V and negligible internal resistance. To conserve the life of the battery, it is desirable that the current drawn from it should be about 10 μA.

(a) Draw a diagram of a suitable circuit, in which the current drawn from the battery is 10 μA. Calculate the values of any resistors used. Show where connections would be made to obtain the 1.2 V output. Label the terminals T+ and T− to indicate their polarity.

(b) A resistor of resistance 1.0 kΩ is now connected across the output terminals. Explain why the output voltage and the current drawn from the battery are affected by making this connection. Determine the new values of output voltage and current drawn.

Unit AS 2:
Waves, Photons and Astronomy

2.1 Waves

You should be able to:

2.1.1   Demonstrate knowledge and understanding of the terms transverse wave and longitudinal wave

2.1.2   Categorise waves as transverse or longitudinal

2.1.3   Analyse graphs to obtain data on amplitude, period, frequency, wavelength and phase

2.1.4   Demonstrate an understanding that polarisation is a phenomenon associated with transverse waves

2.1.5   Recall and use the equations $f = \dfrac{1}{T}$ and $v = f\lambda$

2.1.6   Recall radio waves, microwaves, infrared, visible, ultraviolet, X-rays and gamma rays as regions of the electromagnetic spectrum

2.1.7   State typical wavelengths for each of these regions

2.1.8   Recall that the wavelength of blue light is 400 nm and red light is 700 nm

Waves are everywhere. We encounter sound waves when we listen to a radio, which itself detects radio waves. We see the world around us because our eyes are sensitive to visible light waves. You might even have used a microwave oven to cook your breakfast.

Waves are created by a disturbance which results in a vibration. For example, when a stone is dropped into water it creates ripples (water waves). The water vibrates up and down as the energy from the stone is distributed outwards in all directions. Any object floating on the water will move up and down as the water waves reach it. This means that waves transport energy. The energy is transported to the floating object not by the water but by the wave that is propagated through the water.

A wave that transports energy by causing vibrations in the material or medium through which it moves is called a progressive wave. Progressive waves can be categorised as either transverse or longitudinal, as discussed below.

Mechanical waves, such as sound and water waves, require a substance (medium) through which to travel.

Electromagnetic waves do not require a medium through which to travel.

Transverse and longitudinal waves

In **transverse** waves the vibration of the medium is perpendicular to the direction in which the wave travels (i.e. carries energy or propagates). The following diagram (top of the next page) shows how transverse waves can be sent along a string. The hand is moved up and down as shown. As the transverse wave passes through the medium, the particles vibrate at **right angles** to the direction of propagation of the wave. Electromagnetic waves are transverse waves.

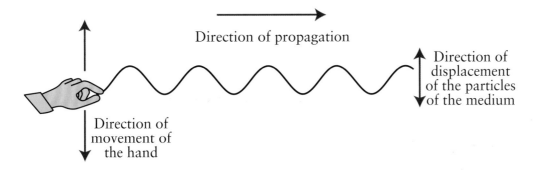

In a **longitudinal** wave the vibrations of the medium are **parallel** to the direction of propagation. The diagram below shows a how a longitudinal wave can be sent along a slinky coil. The hand is moved back and forth as shown. As the longitudinal wave passes through the medium, these coils vibrate parallel to the direction of propagation of the wave.

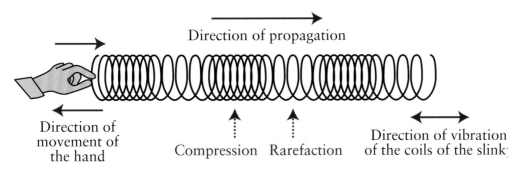

A **compression** is where the coils of the slinky are close together. A **rarefaction** is where the coils are further apart. Sound and ultrasound are longitudinal waves.

Graphical representation of a wave

Both transverse and longitudinal waves can be represented graphically in two ways:

1 Displacement of a particle of the medium against time (below).
2 Displacement of the particles of the medium against distance along the wave (page 92).

Displacement of a particle of the medium against time

This graph shows how the displacement, from its equilibrium position, of a particle of the medium through which the wave is moving, varies with time.

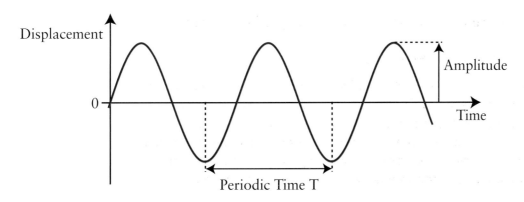

Periodic Time

Period refers to the time which it takes to do something. When an event occurs repeatedly, then we say that the event is periodic and refer to the time for the event to repeat itself as the period.

The period, or Periodic Time T, of a wave is the time taken to make one complete vibrational cycle.

Frequency

The frequency of a wave refers to how often the particles of the medium vibrate when a wave passes through the medium.

The frequency is the number of complete waves that pass a point in one second.

Frequency is measured in hertz, Hz. A frequency of 100 Hz means 100 waves per second pass a point, or that the particle of the medium completes 100 oscillations in one second.

$$\text{Frequency} = \frac{1}{\text{Periodic Time}}$$

Amplitude

The amplitude of a wave refers to the maximum displacement of a particle of the medium from its equilibrium position. You can think of the amplitude as the distance from equilibrium to crest. Similarly, the amplitude can be measured from the equilibrium position to the trough position.

The amount of energy carried by a wave is related to the amplitude of the wave. A high energy wave is characterised by a high amplitude; a low energy wave is characterised by a low amplitude.

Displacement of the particles of the medium against distance along the wave

This graph shows how the displacement, from their equilibrium position, of particles of the medium through which the wave is moving varies with distance along the direction in which the wave is travelling.

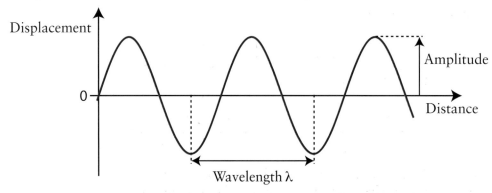

Note: you obtain the period (and hence the frequency) from a **displacement-time** graph. You obtain the wavelength from a **displacement-distance** graph.

Wavelength, λ

The wavelength is defined as the distance the wave form progresses in the periodic time, *T*.

The wavelength can be measured as the distance from crest to next crest or from trough to next trough. In fact, the wavelength of a wave can be measured as the distance from any point on a wave to the corresponding point on the next cycle of the wave. Wavelength is measured in metres.

Phase

The particles of the medium through which a wave passes vibrate. If two particles are vibrating so that at the same instant they are at the same distance and same direction (ie, the same displacement) from their equilibrium positions, they are said to be in phase.

Phase is also used to describe the relative positions of crests and troughs on two waves of the same frequency. If the crests of one wave coincides with the crests of the other, we say the waves are in phase. If the crests of one wave coincide with the troughs of the other, we describe them as being out of phase by ½ λ.

Phase can be expressed in four ways:

- a fraction of a wavelength
- a fraction of a period
- an angle in degrees
- an angle in radians

In general, to find the phase difference in degrees:

$$\text{phase difference} = \frac{x \times 360°}{\lambda} \text{ or } \frac{t \times 360°}{T}$$

and to find the phase difference in radians:

$$\text{phase difference} = \frac{x \times 2\pi}{\lambda} \text{ or } \frac{t \times 2\pi}{T}$$

where x is the distance between the peaks of the two waves and
        t is the time interval between the peaks.

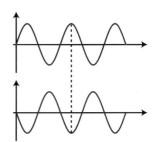 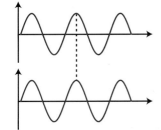 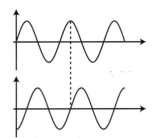

These two waves are out of phase. The crests of one exactly coincide with the troughs of the other. Their phase difference is ½ λ.

These two waves are in phase. The crests of one exactly coincide with the crests of the other.

These two waves are out of phase. The crests of one exactly coincide with the point where the displacement of the other wave is zero. Their phase difference is ¼ λ.

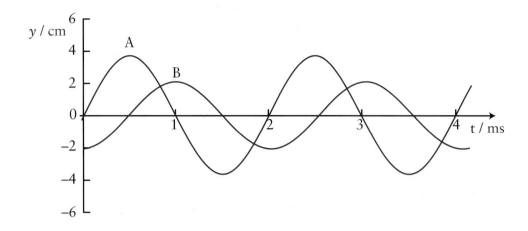

A full wavelength or a full period represents an angle of 360° or 2π radians. Consider the two transverse waves A and B represented by the graph above. What is the phase difference between the waves? The period of each wave is 2 ms.

Wave A reaches its peak after 0.5 ms, wave B reaches its peak after 1.0 ms. So the time interval between the peaks is 0.5 ms.

But this time interval represents ¼ × the period or $\dfrac{T}{4}$.

So the phase difference is ¼ × 360° = 90° or $\dfrac{\pi}{2}$ radians.

Polarisation

A light wave is an electromagnetic wave. Light waves are produced by vibrating electric charges. For the moment, it is sufficient to say that an electromagnetic wave is a transverse wave which has both an electric and a magnetic oscillating component. These two components oscillate in planes that are perpendicular to each other. In the diagram below, the electric component is oscillating in the plane of the page and the magnetic component is oscillating in and out of the page.

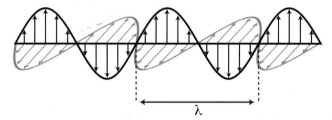

If you could view an electromagnetic wave travelling towards you, then you would observe both the electric component and the magnetic component of the wave occurring in more than one plane of vibration. In this section we will concentrate on the electric component of the electromagnetic wave since it is the component that our eyes are sensitive to.

Only transverse can be polarised

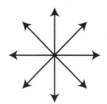

A light wave which is vibrating in more than one plane is referred to as **unpolarised** light. Sunlight and light from a filament lamp are unpolarised. Unpolarised light waves are created by an electric charge which vibrates in a variety of directions, thus creating an electromagnetic wave which oscillates in a variety of directions.

It is possible to change unpolarised light into **polarised** light. Polarised light waves are light waves in which the vibrations occur in a single plane. The process of transforming unpolarised light into polarised light is known as polarisation.

The most common method of polarisation involves the use of a Polaroid filter. A Polaroid filter is able to polarise light because of the chemical composition of the filter material. You can observe the polarisation of light by carrying out the following experiment.

Place a Polaroid filter in front of a filament bulb as shown on the right. The light from the bulb is unpolarised but is plane polarised after passing through the filter. This first filter is called the polariser.

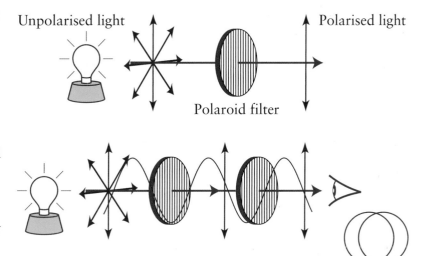

Now view the plane polarised light using a second Polaroid filter. This second filter is known as the analyser. At a certain angle, the light intensity viewed through the second filter will be a maximum.

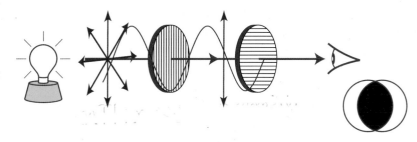

As you rotate the second filter, the intensity of the light will change. You will see that the intensity of the light transmitted by the second filter falls to minimum after it has been rotated 90° from the position at which the intensity was a maximum.

The graph on the right shows how the intensity of the light transmitted by the second polaroid filter changes as this filter is rotated.

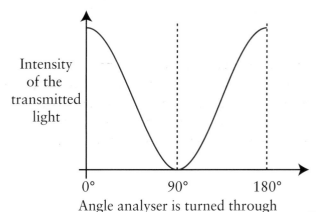

Velocity and period of the wave

The **velocity, v,** of the wave (in m s⁻¹) can be calculated from its wavelength (in m) and frequency using the following equation:

Velocity (v) = Frequency × Wavelength

$$v = f\lambda$$

The **period, T,** of the wave (in s) can be calculated from its frequency (in Hz) using the following equation:

$$\text{Period } (T) = \frac{1}{\text{Frequency}}$$

Spectrum of electromagnetic waves

Electromagnetic waves exist with a very large range of wavelengths. This continuous range of wavelengths is known as the **electromagnetic spectrum**. The entire range of the spectrum is usually broken into specific regions. The subdividing is based mostly on how each region of electromagnetic waves interacts with matter.

The table below shows the electromagnetic spectrum and its various regions. You should note that the boundaries between the different regions of the electromagnetic spectrum are not well defined. However you should have some idea of a typical wavelength for the waves found in each region.

> **Note:** students are required to know that the range of visible light is from 400 nm (violet) to 700 nm (red).
>
> For historical reasons the short wavelength end of the visible spectrum is called the blue end.

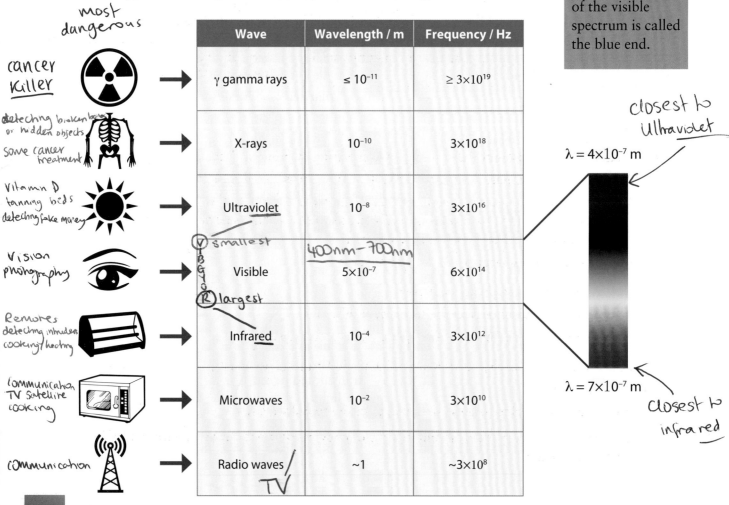

Wave	Wavelength / m	Frequency / Hz
γ gamma rays	$\leq 10^{-11}$	$\geq 3\times10^{19}$
X-rays	10^{-10}	3×10^{18}
Ultraviolet	10^{-8}	3×10^{16}
Visible	5×10^{-7}	6×10^{14}
Infrared	10^{-4}	3×10^{12}
Microwaves	10^{-2}	3×10^{10}
Radio waves	~1	~3×10^8

Handwritten annotations:

most dangerous

cancer killer

detecting broken bones or hidden objects — Some cancer treatment

Vitamin D — tanning beds — detecting fake money

Vision — photography

Removes — detecting intruders — cooking/heating

communication — TV Satellite — cooking

communication

most safe

V smallest — B G Y O R largest

400nm – 700nm

closest to Ultraviolet — $\lambda = 4\times10^{-7}$ m

$\lambda = 7\times10^{-7}$ m — closest to infrared

TV

How electromagnetic waves are generated and their uses

Region of the EM Spectrum	How they are generated	Uses
Radio waves	Electronic circuits in which the electrons are made to vibrate.	Communications, from radio to television.
Microwaves	Electronic circuits in which the electrons are made to vibrate.	Communications Satellite television Cooking food
Infrared	All warm objects emit this type of electromagnetic wave.	Remote controls (e.g. for for TVs) Detecting intruders Cooking and heating
Visible	Hot objects such as filament lamps, flames, the Sun.	Human vision Photography
Ultra-violet	Very hot objects such as the Sun. Gas discharge lamps. Both of these involve exciting the electrons within atoms.	Making vitamin D Sun tan lamps Detecting forged bank notes
X-rays	These are produced when electrons are accelerated to high energy and allowed to strike a metal target. This is the process used in X-ray tubes found in hospitals.	Detecting broken bones Detecting hidden objects (e.g. in luggage) Treatment of some cancers
γ (gamma) rays	Radioactive materials emit gamma rays.	Killing cancerous cells Sterilisation of medical supplies

Exercise 2.1

1 (a) Name the regions of the electromagnetic spectrum in order of decreasing frequency.

   (b) State the approximate limits of the visible part of the electromagnetic spectrum.

   (c) In every transverse wave there is an oscillation perpendicular to the direction in which the wave is moving. State what is oscillating in an electromagnetic wave and illustrate your answer with a suitably labelled diagram.

   (d) State a property unique to electromagnetic waves.

2 (a) What is meant by a polarised wave?

   (b) Explain why light can be polarised but sound cannot.

   (c) How could you test whether the light from a laser is polarised?

3 The speed of sound in dry air at 0°C is 330 m s⁻¹. A tuning fork producing the sound is vibrating at 512 Hz.

   (a) Calculate the period and the wavelength of the sound waves.

   It is thought that the speed of sound in air is directly proportional to the square root of its kelvin temperature.

(b) Calculate the speed of the sound wave from the same fork at 27°C.

(c) What is the wavelength of the waves at 27°C?

4   A wave of amplitude 10 cm and frequency 5 Hz travels along a stretched wire at speed of 20 m s^{-1}.

(a) Calculate the period and sketch a graph of displacement against time to represent the wave.

(b) Calculate the wavelength and sketch a graph of displacement against distance to represent the wave.

(c) Calculate the phase difference between two points on the wire which are 0.8 m apart, giving your answer in degrees.

5   The shortest distance between two points on a progressive wave having a phase difference of 30° is 5 cm. The frequency of the wave is 50 Hz. Calculate the wave speed.

6   A laser emits a single burst of light which lasts for 2 ns. The wavelength of the laser light is 600 nm. How many complete waves are in this burst of laser light?

7   State the period and frequency of the wave shown below.

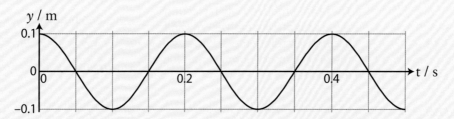

8   Water waves travel 1.20 m across the surface of a lake in a time of 0.6 s. The horizontal distance between two adjacent troughs is 0.8 m. The vertical distance between a crest and a trough is 32 cm.

Calculate (a) the amplitude and (b) the frequency of the waves.

9   (a) Sketch graphs of:

(i) wavelength (in m) against frequency (in Hz) for sound waves in air.

(ii) speed (in m s^{-1}) against wavelength (in m) for electromagnetic waves in air.

(b) A graph is plotted of frequency (in Hz) against λ^{-1} (in m^{-1}) for light waves.
Sketch the graph and find the value of its gradient. Remember the gradient has a unit.

10 There is a constant phase difference between two waves. What does this tell you about:
(a) their frequency?
(b) their wavelength?
(c) their speed?
(d) their amplitudes?

11 A student defines the amplitude of a wave as follows:

"The amplitude of a water wave is the vertical distance between a peak and a trough."

She defines the frequency of the wave as:

"The frequency is the time taken for a particle to make one complete oscillation."

She defines the wavelength as:

"The wavelength is maximum displacement of a particle from its equilibrium position."

She gives the following relationship between velocity, wavelength and period:

"When the frequency, f, is multiplied by the period, T, the answer is always 1."

What, if anything, is wrong with each of these statements?

2.2 Refraction

Refraction occurs when a wave (for example, light) travels from one medium to another (for example, from air into glass). When a light ray is refracted, its direction of travel is changed. The angle between the incident ray and the normal is called the angle of incidence, i. The angle between the normal and the refracted ray is called the angle of refraction, r. Note that the angles are measured from the normal.

Notice that there is also a weak reflected ray. Transparent materials do not allow all the light that is incident to pass through. Glass typically reflects about 4% of the incident light. This weak reflected ray obeys the laws of reflection.

If it slows down, it bends TOWARDS the normal.

Hint: (it'll take a slower time to say towards than away.)

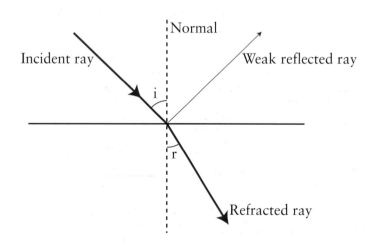

Snell's Law states that:

For light travelling from one medium to another, the ratio $\dfrac{\sin i}{\sin r}$ is a constant.

This constant is known as the **refractive index** of the material.

Experimental verification of Snell's Law and measurement of the refractive index

This can be achieved by **ray tracing** through a glass block.

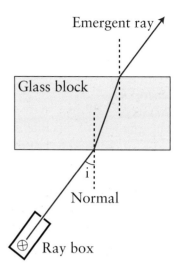

Emergent ray

Glass block

Normal

i

Ray box

1 Place a glass block on a sheet of paper and carefully trace around it.

2 Remove the glass block and mark the normal at one edge. Extend this line into the position of the glass block.

3 Replace the glass block.

4 A ray box is used to produce a narrow ray.

5 Shine the ray into the block so that it meets the block at the point where the normal meets the block.

6 Mark this path carefully with crosses.

7 Mark the emergent ray in a similar fashion.

8 Remove the glass block, join up the crosses to show the incident, refracted and emergent rays.

9 Using a protractor, measure the angles of incidence and refraction.

10 Carefully replace the glass block and repeat this procedure for a number of incident rays with differing angles of incidence.

Results

The table below shows a set of results from such an experiment.

Angle of incidence i / °	Angle of refraction r / °	$\sin (i$ / °$)$	$\sin (r$ / °$)$
10	7.0	0.174	0.122
20	13.5	0.342	0.233
30	20.0	0.500	0.342
40	26.0	0.643	0.438
50	31.5	0.766	0.522
60	36.0	0.866	0.588

A graph of $\sin i$ (y-axis) and $\sin r$ (x-axis) is then drawn (shown on the next page). The straight line through the origin is verification of Snell's Law.

Since the graph is a straight line that passes through the origin, we know that sin i and sin r are proportional.

Or we can state that $\dfrac{\sin i}{\sin r}$ is a constant.

This constant is the refractive index, n

where $n = \dfrac{\sin i}{\sin r}$

The gradient of this line is 1.47, so the refractive index of the material of the block used in the experiment is 1.47.

An alternative to plotting a graph is to calculate the value of $\dfrac{\sin i}{\sin r}$ for each line in the table and to observe that within the limits of the experimental error, the values are constant.

The best value of the refractive index is the mean value of $\dfrac{\sin i}{\sin r}$.

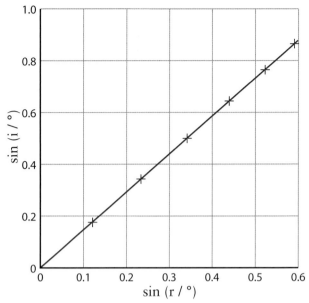

Effect of refraction on speed, wavelength and frequency

When a monochromatic ray of light (monochromatic means consisting of one wavelength only) passes from one material into another, both its speed and its wavelength change. Its frequency does **not** change. The speed and wavelength are related to the refractive index.

The refractive index of a material is a constant. It is the ratio of the speed of light in a vacuum to the speed of light in the material.

$$\text{Refractive index of a material} = \frac{\text{speed of light in vacuum}}{\text{speed of light in material}}$$

The speed of light in a vacuum is almost equal to the speed of light in air. This means that the refractive index for light travelling from vacuum to glass is for most practical purposes the same as that for light travelling from air to glass.

Say the refractive index for light travelling from air into glass is 1.5.

$$1.5 = \frac{\text{speed of light in vacuum}}{\text{speed of light in glass}}$$

This tells us that the speed of light in this glass is 2×10^8 m s^{-1}.

When a ray of light enters or leaves a transparent material along the normal, the angle of incidence $i = 0°$ and the angle of refraction $r = 0°$. However the light's speed **does** change. For example, travelling from air into glass the speed decreases. Travelling from glass into air, the speed and wavelength increase. But the frequency of the light does not change.

Relationship between refractive indices

The diagram on the right shows a ray of light passing from air into glass. The refractive index can be written as:

$$_{air}n_{glass} = \frac{\sin i}{\sin r}$$

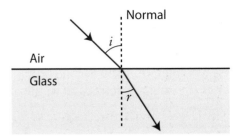

If the path of the ray were reversed, i.e. glass to air, the refractive index for glass to air can be written as:

$$_{glass}n_{air} = \frac{\sin r}{\sin i}$$

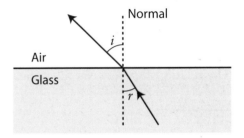

Examination of the two relationships shows that:

$$_{air}n_{glass} = \frac{1}{_{glass}n_{air}}$$

Thus, when travelling from air to glass and back to air: $_{a}n_{g} \times _{g}n_{a} = 1$

In general, $_{a}n_{g} \times _{g}n_{w} \times _{w}n_{p} \times _{p}n_{a} = 1$

where the letter a represents air (or vacuum), and g, w and p represent three different media (such as glass, water and perspex). Note the symmetry in the equation – the material between the letters marked n must be the same and the material at the start and the end is always air.

Worked Example

1 Given that $_{air}n_{glass} = {}^{3}/_{2}$ and $_{air}n_{water} = {}^{4}/_{3}$, find $_{water}n_{glass}$.

Solution

$$_{g}n_{a} = \frac{1}{_{a}n_{g}} = \frac{1}{^{3}/_{2}} = {}^{2}/_{3}$$

Using: $\quad _{a}n_{w} \times _{w}n_{g} \times _{g}n_{a} = 1$

$$^{4}/_{3} \times _{w}n_{g} \times {}^{2}/_{3} = 1$$

So: $\quad _{w}n_{g} = {}^{9}/_{8}$

Critical angle

Consider what happens when light travels from a material of high refractive index to one of lower refractive index, for example, from glass into air. As the angle of incidence in the glass increases so does the angle of refraction in the air.

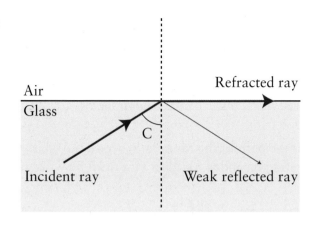

The largest angle of refraction is 90°. The angle of incidence in the glass that produces this angle of refraction of 90° is called the **critical angle C**. Note that there is still a weak reflected ray.

The value of the critical angle depends on the refractive index of the material.

The relationship between the critical angle and the refractive index of the material can be derived by applying Snell's law.

$$_{glass}n_{air} = \frac{\sin C}{\sin 90} = \sin C$$

$$_{glass}n_{air} = \frac{1}{_{air}n_{glass}}$$

$$\sin C = \frac{1}{_{air}n_{glass}}$$

Total internal reflection

When the angle of incidence in the material with the higher refractive index is greater than the critical angle, a phenomenon known as **total internal reflection** occurs. Total internal reflection involves the reflection of all the incident light at the boundary between two materials.

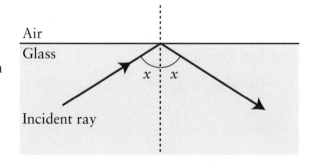

Remember, total internal reflection takes place only when **both** of the following two conditions are met:

1 The direction of the light is from one material to one of **lower** refractive index.
2 The angle of incidence in the material of higher refractive index is **greater** than the critical angle.

Therefore, total internal reflection is possible for light travelling from water towards air, but it will not happen for light travelling from air towards water. Total internal reflection is possible for light travelling from glass to water but not from water to glass.

A right angled prism can be used to deviate a ray of light by 90° using total internal reflection as shown in the diagram. The ray meets the side AB along the normal so no refraction takes place and the ray continues into the glass. When it reaches the side AC the angle of incidence from glass to air is 45°. The critical angle for the glass in this example is 42°, so total internal reflection takes place. Finally the ray travels to side BC and since it meets it along the normal, no refraction takes place and the ray emerges into the air.

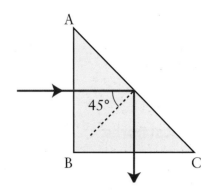

Measuring the refractive index using total internal reflection

Total internal reflection can be demonstrated using a semi-circular glass block as shown below. This method also provides us with a way to measure the refractive index, although it must be stated that it is not a very accurate one.

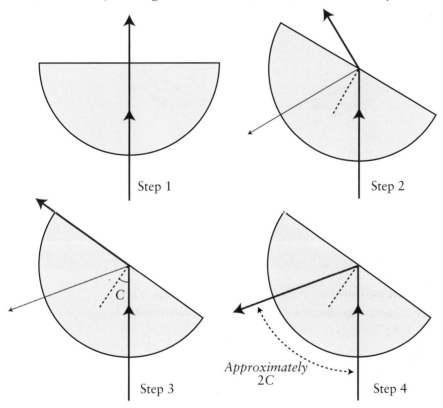

1 A ray is directed towards the centre of a semi-circular glass block. This ensures that there is no refraction at the curved edge. The ray of light meets the curve at right angles.

2 The block is slowly rotated. The emergent ray is now bent away from the normal as shown. Note the weak reflected ray.

3 At a particular angle, the critical angle, the emergent ray is refracted at an angle of 90° to the normal. It travels along the straight edge of the glass block. This can be difficult to see.

4 However, if the angle the incident ray makes with the straight edge of the glass is increased by a very small amount, total internal reflection takes place. This is very noticeable since the weak reflected ray suddenly becomes bright.

The angle between the two rays is now just slightly greater than 2C. Measure this angle and use the value to calculate an approximate value for the refractive index using the equation below.

$$\sin C = \frac{1}{_{air}n_{glass}}$$

Optical fibres

The use of a long strand of glass to send light from one end of the medium to the other is the basis for modern day use of **optical fibres**. Optical fibres are used in communication systems and micro-surgery. On each occasion when the ray of light meets the glass/air boundary the angle of incidence exceeds the critical angle, and total internal reflection takes place. None of the incident energy is ever lost due to the transmission of light across the boundary. The intensity of the signal remains constant.

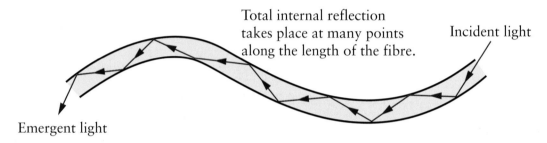

Total internal reflection takes place at many points along the length of the fibre.

Incident light

Emergent light

The step index fibre

The step index fibre consists of a glass core, typically 100 μm in diameter, surrounded by a glass cladding, typically 150 μm in diameter. Surrounding the core and cladding is a layer of protective plastic called a sheath, which is usually omitted from diagrams.

The refractive index of the core is slightly greater than that of the cladding. This type of optical fibre is called 'step index' because the refractive index does not change gradually at the core/cladding boundary, rather it changes like a step.

Provided the angle of incidence at the core/cladding boundary is greater than the critical angle, the light signal is propagated in the core by repeated total internal reflection.

The path of light along the centre of the core is called axial mode. The path of light that repeatedly meets the core/cladding boundary at the critical angle is called the highest order mode. There is clearly a difference between the time taken for light to travel up a fibre along the central axis and that travelling by repeated total internal reflections at just above the critical angle. This is called modal dispersion and is very undesirable. In an endoscope, modal dispersion would result in a blurred image of the target organ. Modal dispersion can be prevented by using **very thin cores** so that only axial mode is possible.

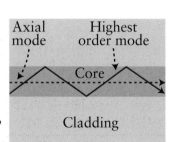

Axial mode — Highest order mode — Core — Cladding

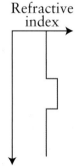

Refractive index

Worked Example

1 An optical fibre has a core of refractive index of 1.6 and a cladding of refractive index 1.5.

   (a) Calculate the critical angle at the core/cladding boundary in this fibre.

   (b) Calculate the ratio of the path length for the highest order mode to the axial mode in this fibre.

   (c) What is the time difference between a light signal travelling along the axis of a 1 km length of this fibre and that of a signal travelling in the highest order mode?

Solution

(a) $_{air}n_{cladding} \times _{cladding}n_{core} \times _{core}n_{air} = 1$

$1.5 \times _{cladding}n_{core} \times ^1/_{1.6} = 1$

$_{cladding}n_{core} = {^{1.6}}/_{1.5} = 1.067$

critical angle $C = \sin^{-1}(\dfrac{1}{_{cladding}n_{core}}) = \sin^{-1}(\dfrac{1}{1.067}) = 69.6°$

(b) Suppose the axial mode distance corresponding to a single total internal reflection is x. Then the corresponding highest order mode distance is $(\dfrac{x}{\sin C})$.

So the required ratio is $\dfrac{1}{\sin C}$ or $\dfrac{1}{\sin 69.6} = 1.07$

(c) Speed of light in the core $= \dfrac{\text{speed in air}}{_{air}n_{core}} = \dfrac{3 \times 10^8}{1.6} = 1.875 \times 10^8$ m s^{-1}

Distance travelled in axial mode = 1000 m

Time for axial mode signal $= \dfrac{1000}{1.875 \times 10^8} = 5.333$ μs

Distance travelled in highest order mode = $1000 \times 1.07 = 1070$ m

Time for highest order mode signal $= \dfrac{1070}{1.875 \times 10^8} = 5.707$ μs

Time difference = 0.374 μs

Note: the most common mistake in part (c) is failing to find the speed of light in the core.

Optical fibres in medicine – the flexible endoscope

An endoscope is a flexible tube that allows us to look into the body. In many cases there is no need to perform surgery to do this. In other cases, a small incision is required to perform what has become known as key-hole surgery.

The endoscope has two bundles of optical fibres. One is called the **illumination bundle** and carries light to the object being viewed. The other bundle, the **image bundle**, carries back the reflected light. The optical fibres inside the image bundle are carefully arranged parallel to each other to create what is termed a **coherent bundle**.

The image is viewed or photographed through a magnifying eyepiece. In some instances a TV camera is attached and the image displayed on a monitor.

When inserted through the mouth, the endoscope can be used to view the gastrointestinal tract (oesophagus, stomach and duodenum). Alternatively, in the technique called laparoscopy, the endoscope is inserted through the wall of the abdomen to study the liver, spleen and other organs. The information obtained in this way provides direct and often very clear evidence of bleeding ulcers, constrictions, benign and malignant tumours and cirrhosis of the liver.

The endoscope also allows a range of minor surgical treatments. **Forceps** attached at the viewing end allows a surgeon to **remove a sample of tissue (biopsy)** for detailed analysis. Electrodes can be used to apply heat to stop bleeding. A range of **extractors** can be fitted and used to remove foreign objects from the throat or possibly drugs hidden in the lower bowel of smugglers. There is also a **water channel** to wash away the mucus from the end of the endoscope within the body.

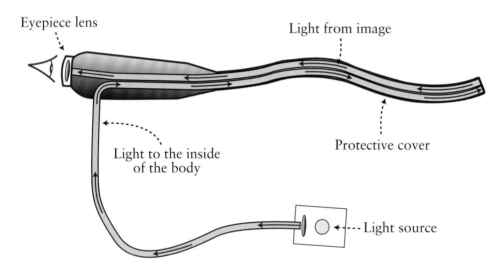

Optical fibres in industry

The principles of industrial and medical endoscopes are similar. The differences are the applications and the associated tools. Industrial endoscopes are usually called borescopes and they are often used to view what is happening in inaccessible sites. A brief list of the applications is shown in the table below.

Industry	Application
Car	Inspection and repair of cylinders, exhaust pipes, manifolds, etc
Aircraft	Inspection and repair of engines, shafts, landing gear, turbines, etc
Ships	Inspection and repair of engines, turbines, heat exchangers, pipe lines, etc
Electricity generation	Inspection for cracks on mechanical equipment, boilers, turbines, pipes, etc
Espionage	Secretly viewing what is happening in another room
General	Internal check of pipes, tanks, steel pipes, etc

Exercise 2.2

1 (a) The refractive index of diamond is 2.419 for light of wavelength 589.3 nm. Explain what this statement means.

   (b) Find the critical angle of diamond at this wavelength.

   (c) Describe whether the refractive index of diamond at higher wavelengths would be bigger than, smaller than or equal to 2.419. Give a reason for your answer.

2 A ray of light travels from inside a block of transparent material towards the air. The refractive index of the material of the block is 1.40. The ray emerges from the block into the air at an angle of 47.0° to the block.

   Calculate the minimum increase in the angle of the ray inside the block to cause this ray to undergo total internal reflection.

3 The diagram below shows refraction at the surface of a liquid. If the refractive index of the liquid is 1.33, find the size of the angle marked x.

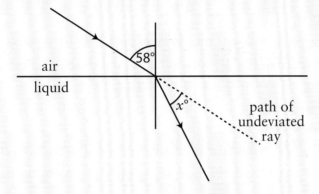

4 The experimental data below shows the angles of incidence in air and the corresponding angles of refraction in water.

Angle of incidence in air, i / °	20.0	30.0	40.0	50.0	60.0	70.0	80.0
Angle of refraction in water, r / °	15.0	22.1	28.8	35.1	40.6	45.3	48.2

   (a) Use the data to draw a suitable straight line graph from which the refractive index of water might be found. You will need to copy the table above and complete it. Be sure to label the table headings and the graph axes correctly. The third and fourth rows have been left blank for your use.

   (b) Use your graph to find the refractive index of water with respect to air, $_a n_w$.

   (c) Use your answer to part (b) to find the critical angle for water.

5 The diagram on the right shows a ray of light incident at an angle of 75° at one side of a block of transparent material.

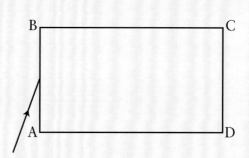

The ray enters the glass and meets the adjacent side, BC. The refractive index of the material from which the block is made is 1.524.

(a) Calculate the angle of refraction at face AB.

(b) Calculate the angle of incidence at face BC.

(c) Describe what happens at BC. Justify your answer with suitable calculations.

6 Write a detailed account of an experiment to find the critical angle of the material of a semi-circular perspex block.

7 (a) What is a step index optical fibre?

The refractive index of the core of an optical fibre is 1.6 and the critical angle at the core/cladding boundary is 60°.

(b) Calculate the refractive index of the core/cladding boundary with respect to the air.

(c) Calculate the time difference between a light signal travelling along the axis of a 500 m fibre and that of a signal travelling in the highest order mode.

(d) An engineer is seeking to minimise the time delay calculated in (c) by changing the cladding which surrounds the core.

   (i) In what way, if any, would the refractive index of the cladding change?

   (ii) What effect, if any, would this have on the critical angle at the core/cladding boundary?

   (iii) Carefully explain the advantage of using cores of a smaller diameter.

2.3 Lenses

You should be able to:

2.3.1 Draw ray diagrams for converging and diverging lenses

2.3.2 Use the equation $\frac{1}{u} + \frac{1}{v} = \frac{1}{f}$ for converging and diverging lenses

2.3.3 Verify experimentally the lens equation and the evaluation of f, the focal length of a converging lens, for real images only

2.3.4 Define m as the ratio of the image height to the object height or $m = \frac{h_i}{h_o}$

2.3.5 Recall and use the equation $m = \frac{v}{u}$

2.3.6 Describe the use of lenses to correct myopia and hypermetropia

2.3.7 Perform calculations on the correction of long and short sight, including a calculation of the new range of vision

2.3.8 Perform calculations involving the power of lenses

$$M = \frac{V}{U}$$

$$M = \frac{H_i}{H_o}$$

$$\frac{1}{U} + \frac{1}{V} = \frac{1}{f}$$

A lens consists of a piece of glass or other transparent material with one or two curved surfaces. Lenses can be classified into **converging** (**convex**) and **diverging** (**concave**). The effect of these two types of lens on a parallel beam of light is shown below.

When parallel rays of light pass through a converging lens they are refracted so that they pass through the focal point or principal focus of the lens. This type of principal focus is described as **real**.

In the case of a diverging lens the parallel rays are refracted so that they spread out (diverge) from the focal point or principal focus of the concave lens. This type of principal focus is described as **virtual**.

The distance from the centre of a lens to the focal point is the **focal length f.**

Converging or convex lens

Diverging or concave lens

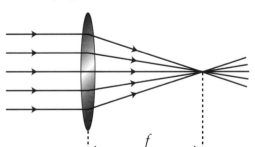

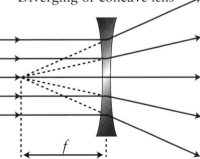

Focal point (principal focus): point on principle axis to which rays parallel and close to axis converge after going through lens

Images formed by converging lenses

The apparatus shown below can be used to investigate how the image formed on the screen by the converging lens changes as the distance between the lens and the illuminated wire mesh on the lamphouse is altered.

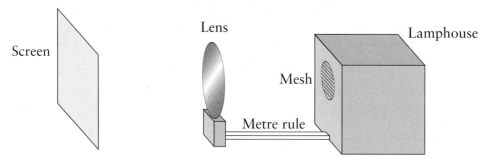

You should initially place the lamphouse at a distance from the lens of approximately three times the focal length of the lens. An approximate method for the focal length can be found using the procedure described on page 116.

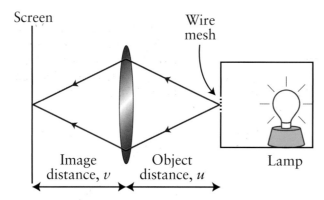

The screen is then moved until a sharp image is obtained. The lamphouse is gradually moved closer to the lens and for a number of positions the screen is re-positioned until the image is again sharp.

Converging lens: ray diagrams

To find the position, size and nature of the image formed by a convex lens we need to find where at least two rays of light meet having passed through the lens from the object. The diagrams on the following pages show what happens to three particular rays when they pass through a convex lens. In the diagram the thickness of the lens is ignored: the lens is represented by a straight line (dashed). All refraction happens at this line, the 'curved lens' shape simply identifies the type of lens.

The horizontal line that passes through the optical centre of the lens is called the principal axis. On each side of the lens the focus F is marked and a point at twice this distance from the lens, $2F$, is also marked. The object is small and upright and sits on the principal axis at various distances from the lens.

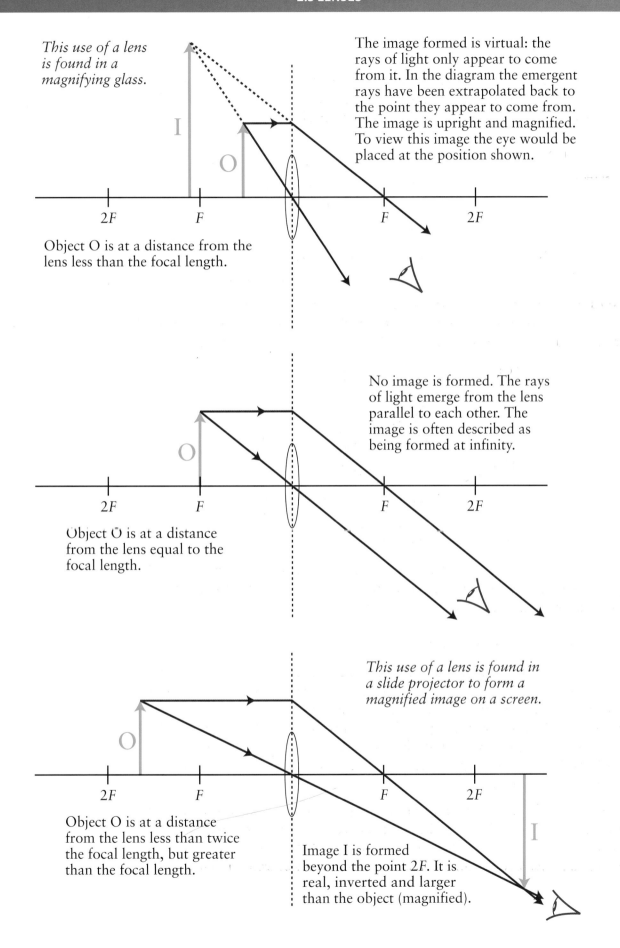

This use of a lens is found in a magnifying glass.

The image formed is virtual: the rays of light only appear to come from it. In the diagram the emergent rays have been extrapolated back to the point they appear to come from. The image is upright and magnified. To view this image the eye would be placed at the position shown.

Object O is at a distance from the lens less than the focal length.

No image is formed. The rays of light emerge from the lens parallel to each other. The image is often described as being formed at infinity.

Object O is at a distance from the lens equal to the focal length.

This use of a lens is found in a slide projector to form a magnified image on a screen.

Object O is at a distance from the lens less than twice the focal length, but greater than the focal length.

Image I is formed beyond the point 2F. It is real, inverted and larger than the object (magnified).

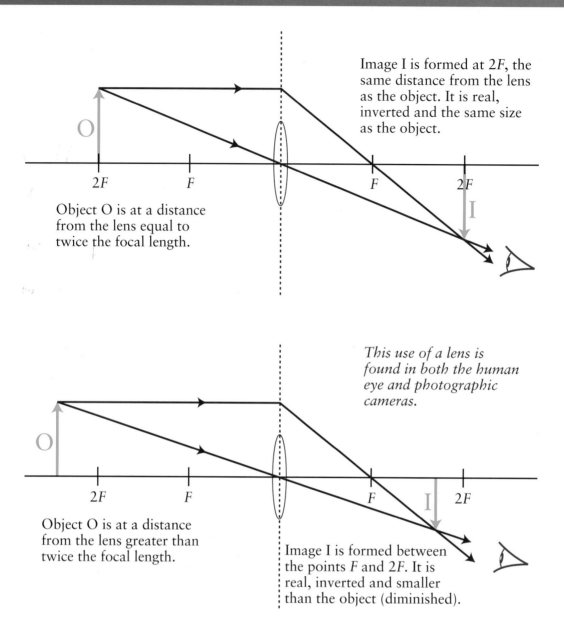

Image I is formed at 2F, the same distance from the lens as the object. It is real, inverted and the same size as the object.

Object O is at a distance from the lens equal to twice the focal length.

This use of a lens is found in both the human eye and photographic cameras.

Object O is at a distance from the lens greater than twice the focal length.

Image I is formed between the points F and 2F. It is real, inverted and smaller than the object (diminished).

Summary for converging lenses

Converging Lens: (handwritten)

Note: you must memorise this table.

Position of object	Position of image	Nature of the Image		
		Real / virtual	**Enlarged / diminished**	**Upright / inverted**
Between F and the lens	Further from the lens than the object and on the same side of the lens	Virtual	Enlarged _(but diverging will be diminished ✗)_	Upright
At F	At ∞	Real	Enlarged	Inverted
Between F and $2F$	Beyond $2F$	Real	Enlarged	Inverted
At $2F$	At $2F$	Real	Same size as the object	Inverted
Beyond $2F$	Between F and $2F$	Real	Diminished	Inverted
At ∞	At F	Real	Diminished	Inverted

Diverging lens: ray diagrams

And diverging is always virtual, upright + diminished. (handwritten)

A ray parallel to the principal axis will appear to come from the focus after refraction by the lens.

A ray through the optical centre of the lens will pass through without deviation.

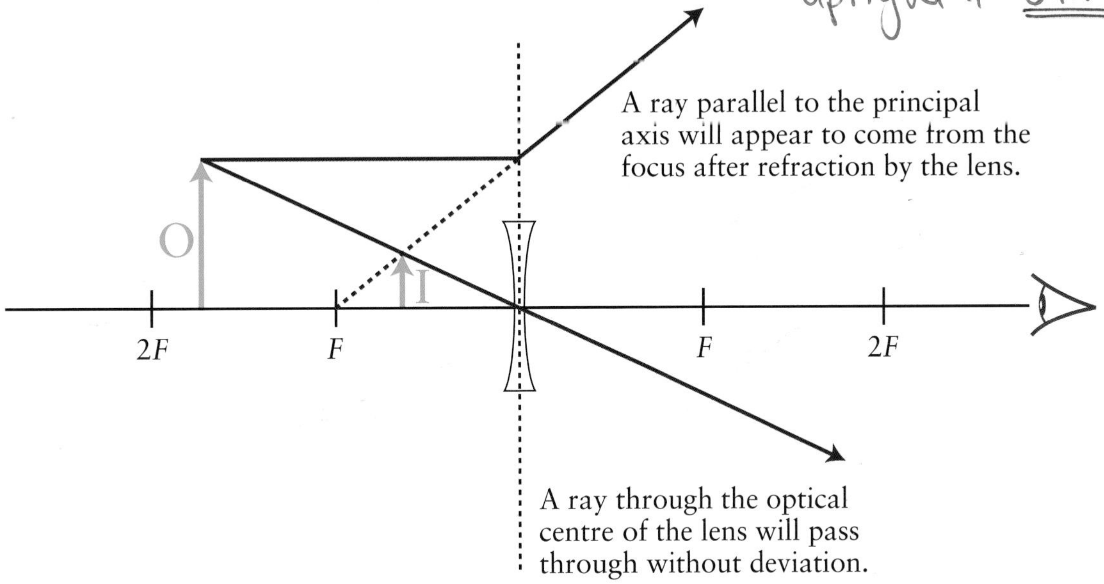

The image of a real object in a diverging lens is **always** virtual. With the exception of the ray through the optical centre of the lens, all other rays only appear to come from the image. The image is **upright and diminished**. These are properties of the image formed by a concave lens **regardless of the position of the object**. The two rays shown in the diagram above can be used to locate the image for all positions of the object.

always draw virtual rays with a dotted line. (handwritten)

Measurement of the focal length of a converging lens

1 Approximate method – using a distant object

Light from a distant object, more than 10 m away, is approximately parallel. A convex lens will form an image of this object at approximately the focus.

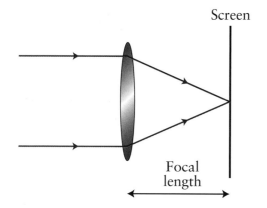

Arrange the lens so that the image of a such an object is formed on a screen. Adjust the distance from the lens to the screen so that image is as sharp as possible.

Measure this distance; it is approximately the focal length. This should be repeated a number of times and the average taken.

2 Using a plane mirror

If an illuminated object is placed at the focus of a convex lens the light emerging from the lens is parallel. If these parallel rays are reflected back upon themselves, by a plane mirror, an image is formed beside the object.

The object is an illuminated wire mesh.

Place the plane mirror as close as possible to the lens. Move the lens and plane mirror together until a sharp image of the wire mesh appears on the front of the lamp house. Measure the distance from the lens to the lamp house; this is the focal length of the lens. The reliability of the result can be improved by repeating the above process and taking an average.

3 Measuring object and image distance

This method also allows you to verify an important relationship between the object distance, the image distance and the focal length: the **lens formula**. As before, the object is the illuminated wire mesh.

To ensure that the image is real, allowing it to be obtained on a screen, the object must be a distance from the lens greater than the focal length of the lens. Measure the distance from the mesh to the lens; this is the object distance u.

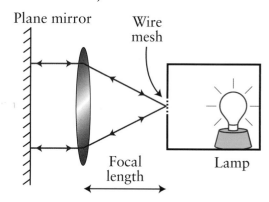

The position of the screen is adjusted until a sharp image is produced on the screen.

The distance from the lens to the screen is measured; this is the image distance v. The process is repeated for a series of different values of the object distance u, measuring the image distance v for each one. Values of u and v are tabulated and values of $\frac{1}{u}$ and $\frac{1}{v}$ calculated and tabulated.

A typical set of values is shown in the table below.

Object distance u / m	Image distance v / m	$\frac{1}{u}$ / m^{-1}	$\frac{1}{v}$ / m^{-1}	$\left(\frac{1}{u} + \frac{1}{v}\right)$ / m^{-1}
0.400	0.133	2.50	7.52	10.02
0.350	0.140	2.86	7.14	10.00
0.300	0.150	3.33	6.67	10.00
0.250	0.167	4.00	5.99	9.99
0.200	0.196	5.00	5.10	10.10
0.150	0.300	6.67	3.33	10.00
Average value of $\left(\frac{1}{u} + \frac{1}{v}\right)$ / m^{-1}				10.02
Average value of focal length / m				0.10

Notice, allowing for experimental uncertainty, the values of $\frac{1}{u} + \frac{1}{v}$ = constant.

This constant is $\frac{1}{f}$.

By finding the reciprocal of the average value of $\frac{1}{u} + \frac{1}{v}$, we see that the focal length of this lens is 0.10 m.

The relationship between u, v and f is known as the lens formula and is written as:

$$\frac{1}{u} + \frac{1}{v} = \frac{1}{f}$$

Graphical analysis

The graph of object distance u against image distance v is a curve, as shown opposite. To find the focal length, a straight line $v = u$ is drawn. The path of the straight line is determined by points where the object distance equals the image distance.

If you examine the ray diagrams for the convex lens you will see that the only situation when $u = v$ is when the object is at a distance equal to twice the focal length. The resulting image is also at a distance of twice the focal length from the lens.

Where the dotted line v = u crosses the curve, the values of u and v represent **twice** the focal length. In this case the lines intersect at $v = u = 0.2$ m, so the focal length is ½ × 0.20 = 0.10 m

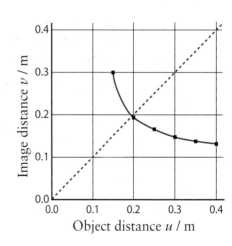

A better approach is to use the results to plot a linear graph. This is achieved by plotting $\frac{1}{v}$ against $\frac{1}{u}$ and **ruling the line of best fit to the data points.**

Since $\frac{1}{u} + \frac{1}{v} = \frac{1}{f}$, then rearranging gives:

$$\frac{1}{v} = \frac{-1}{u} + \frac{1}{f}$$

And mapping to the general equation for a straight line gives:

$$\frac{1}{v} = -1 \times \frac{1}{u} + \frac{1}{f}$$
$$y = m \quad\quad x \quad + \quad c$$

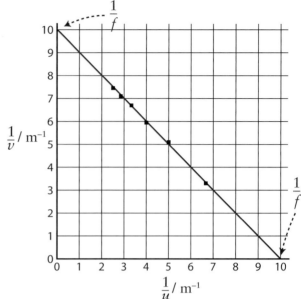

So the graph of $\frac{1}{v}$ against $\frac{1}{u}$ is a straight line of gradient –1 and vertical axis intercept $\frac{1}{f}$, as shown in the graph.

Note that if $\frac{1}{v} = 0$, then $\frac{1}{u} = \frac{1}{f}$. So the intercept on the horizontal axis is also $\frac{1}{f}$.

The intercept on each axis provides a value for $\frac{1}{f}$.

The most reliable value for f is the reciprocal of the mean value of $\frac{1}{f}$ from the two intercepts.

Verification of the lens formula, $\frac{1}{u} + \frac{1}{v} = \frac{1}{f}$, comes from observing that:

- the graph of $\frac{1}{v}$ against $\frac{1}{v}$ is a straight line of gradient –1, and

- the value of f found from the intercepts of this graph agrees with the value of f found by a second independent method, as described earlier in the chapter.

Finding the position, size and nature of the image formed by a lens

The position, size and nature of the image formed by a lens can be determined in two ways:

1 accurate ray drawing

2 use of the lens formula, $\frac{1}{u} + \frac{1}{v} = \frac{1}{f}$

Real/virtual sign convention

When using the lens formula, you must apply a sign convention to each of the distances involved.

A real image is one that rays of light actually pass through. The distance to a real object, real image or real focal point is positive.

A virtual image is one that rays of light only appear to pass through. The distance to a virtual object, virtual image or virtual focal point is negative.

Consequently, the focal length of a converging lens is positive and the focal length of a diverging lens is negative.

Magnification

We define the linear magnification of an image as the ratio of the image height to the object height or:

$$m = \frac{h_i}{h_o}$$

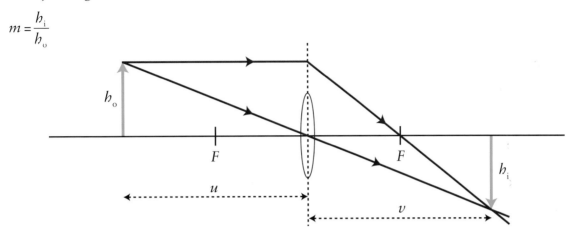

By using the properties of similar triangles, we can show that magnification is also equal to the ratio of the image distance to the object distance. So:

$$m = \frac{h_i}{h_o} = \frac{v}{u}$$

Note: you must remember this equation.

Power of a lens

The power of lens is defined as: power $- \dfrac{1}{f}$

The focal length, f, is given in metres, so the power is measured in m^{-1} or **dioptres**, symbol D.

A diverging lens has a negative power, a converging lens has a positive power.

Exercise 2.3A

1 A convex lens produces a real image of linear magnification 1.

 (a) (i) Explain what this statement means.

 (ii) Draw a ray diagram to show how this image has been formed. Use appropriate arrows on the rays of light.

 (b) A certain lens forms an upright image of an object. The image is located 25 cm from the lens and its linear magnification is 0.5.

 (i) What type of lens is used?

 (ii) Is the image real or virtual?

 (iii) Calculate the position of the object relative to the lens.

 (iv) Calculate the focal length and the power of the lens.

2 (a) Draw diagrams to illustrate what is meant by:

  (i) the principal focus of a converging lens.

  (ii) the principal focus of a diverging lens.

  (b) The distance between the principal focus and the optical centre of a converging lens is 150 mm. An object is placed 50 mm from this lens.

  (i) Show that the distance between the object and its image is 25 mm.

  (ii) Show that the linear magnification of the image is 1.5.

  (iii) Which two of the following words best describe the image?

  real   erect   virtual   inverted

3 (a) An object, OA, is placed perpendicular to the principal axis of a converging lens of focal length 200 mm so that a virtual image is produced 250 mm from the lens.

  (i) Calculate the position of the object and the magnification of the image.

  (ii) Illustrate your answer to (i) with a ray diagram.

  (b) A diverging lens has a focal length of 200 mm. An object 20 mm tall is placed 250 mm from the lens.

  (i) Calculate the distance between the object and the image.

  (ii) Calculate the height of the image.

4 A lamphouse is placed 1250 mm from a screen. When a converging lens is placed some distance from the crosswires on the lamphouse, a sharp image is observed on the screen. The lens is now moved 250 mm closer to the screen but the position of the screen and lamphouse is unchanged. When this happens a sharp image of the crosswires is seen on the screen once more. Calculate the focal length of the lens.

5 You are supplied with a converging lens of focal length 20.0 cm, an illuminated object, a white screen and a metre rule. Suppose you are asked to carry out an experiment to verify the lens equation $\frac{1}{u} + \frac{1}{v} = \frac{1}{f}$, where the symbols have their usual meaning.

  (a) Draw a diagram to show how you would set up the apparatus.

  (b) State clearly what you would do and the readings you would take.

  (c) State what graph you would plot to verify the lens equation.

  (d) Explain in detail how your graph verifies the lens equation.

6 An object is placed 100 mm from a converging lens. A sharp, real image is observed on the other side of the lens and 100 mm from the optical centre. State the focal length of the lens and the linear magnification of the image.

7 A diverging lens of focal length 120 mm produces an image at a distance of 40 mm from its optical centre.

  (a) Calculate the distance between the object and the lens.

  (b) The object is 12 cm tall. What height is the image?

(c) Which three of the following words best describe the image?

diminished   real   enlarged   virtual   erect   inverted

Defects of vision

The human eye has a lens which can alter its focal length. It does this by altering its shape: thick to give a short focal length (high power) for focussing on near objects and thin for a long focal length (low power) for focussing on distant objects. This ability of the eye to see objects clearly at different distances is known as **accommodation. Most of the refraction of the light takes place at the boundary between the air and the cornea** because this is where the largest change in refractive index occurs.

The farthest point which can be seen clearly by the unaided eye is called the **far point**. For the normal eye this is at infinity. Light from the far point reaches the eye as parallel rays. The rays are refracted by the eye so that they meet on the retina forming a sharp image of the distant object.

The nearest point which can be seen clearly by the unaided eye is called the **near point**. For the normal eye this is at 25 cm. The light from the near point reaches the eye as diverging rays. These are refracted by the eye so that they meet on the retina forming a sharp image of the object at the near point.

Myopia

Myopia needs diverging → to remember, diverging is a SHORTER word, hence short-sighted

A person who suffers from myopia (short sight) is unable to see distant objects sharply.

They cannot make the lens thin enough to view distant objects. This causes the light from distant objects to converge towards a point in front of the retina. The image seen by the person is blurred.

The person's far point is much closer to the eye than the normal infinite distance. It might be only a few metres or possibly less.

Light from this point is correctly focused by the eye so that a sharp image of an object at this point is obtained.

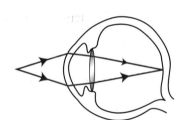

Person's far point

To correct this defect a concave (diverging) lens is used. The focal length of the lens is equal to the distance to the person's actual far point. This means that parallel rays of light from a distant object are refracted so that they appear to diverge from the person's far point.

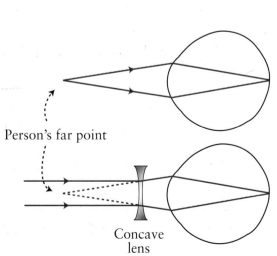

Concave lens

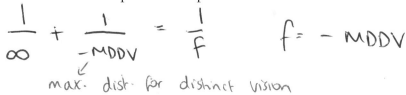

$$\frac{1}{\infty} + \frac{1}{-MDDV} = \frac{1}{f} \qquad f = -MDDV$$

max. dist. for distinct vision

Worked Examples

A girl's near point is 25 cm from her eye, but her far point is at 400 cm.

1 From what defect of vision is the girl suffering?

Solution

Myopia (short sight).

2 What type of lens should be prescribed to help her see distant objects?

Solution

A diverging (concave) lens.

3 What is the power of this lens?

Solution

An object placed at infinity must give a virtual image at the girl's unaided far point (400 cm). So $f = -400$ cm (minus because it is a diverging lens).

$$P = \frac{1}{f} + \frac{1}{-4} = -0.25 \text{ D}$$

4 What is her range of vision when using spectacles fitted with this lens?

Solution

We must now find the girl's least distance of distinct vision when using this lens.

To do this we find the position of the real object which would give a virtual image at her (normal) near point (25 cm).

$$\frac{1}{u} + \frac{1}{v} = \frac{1}{f}$$

$$\frac{1}{u} + \frac{1}{-25} = \frac{1}{(-400)}$$

$$\frac{1}{u} = \frac{15}{(400)} \text{ giving } u = 26.7 \text{ cm}$$

So, with the diverging lens the girl's range of vision is from 26.7 cm to ∞.

Without the diverging lens her range of vision was 25 cm to 400 cm.

HINT: converging is a longer word and hence long-sighted.

Hypermetropia

Converging needed

This is also known as long sight. A long sighted person sees distant objects clearly but does not see near objects clearly. This happens because the ciliary muscles are too weak to make the lens thick and so have a shorter focal length.

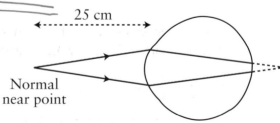

25 cm

Normal near point

An object held at the normal near point distance of 25 cm will not be seen clearly. The rays of light from the object are not bent sufficiently to form an image on the retina.

$$\frac{1}{0.25} + \frac{1}{-LDDV} = \frac{1}{f}$$

least distance for distinct vision

The near point is much further than 25 cm. Rays of light from an object placed at their near point are bent so that they meet on the retina resulting in the object being seen clearly.

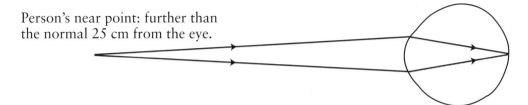

Person's near point: further than the normal 25 cm from the eye.

To correct for this defect a convex lens is used. The focal length of this lens has to be such that an object at 25 cm appears to be at the person's near point. If a person has a near point at 100 cm then for an object at 25 cm the convex lens has to create a virtual image at 100 cm of an object at 25 cm.

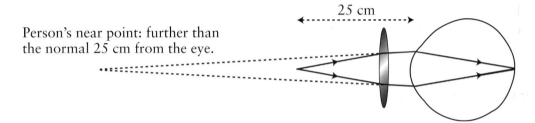

Person's near point: further than the normal 25 cm from the eye.

The use of a converging lens means that the object that is really at 25 cm from the eye appears to be 100 cm from the eye. The converging lens forms a virtual image at the person's near point. The lens formula is used to find the focal length of the lens. If the person's near point is 100 cm from his eye then we have:

$$\frac{1}{u} + \frac{1}{v} = \frac{1}{f}$$ Substitution of values gives: $\frac{1}{25} + \frac{1}{(-100)} = \frac{1}{f}$

The negative sign is used because the image at the person's near point is virtual. The lens has a focal length value of 33.3 cm and a power of +3.0 D.

Worked Examples

A man with hypermetropia has an unaided near point of 50 cm and a far point of infinity.

1 What is the power of lens needed to correct the hypermetropia?

Solution

The converging lenses have a focal length so that an object at the normal near point (25 cm) would give a virtual image at the unaided near point (50 cm).

$$\frac{1}{f} = \frac{1}{u} + \frac{1}{v} \text{ so, } \quad \frac{1}{f} = \frac{1}{25} + \frac{1}{(-50)} = \frac{1}{50}$$

so, $f = 50$ cm and $P = \frac{1}{0.5} = +2$ D

2 What is the range of his vision when he wears these lenses?

Solution

An object placed 50 cm from this convex lens would give rise to a (virtual) image at infinity. The man therefore has a range of vision of 25 cm to 50 cm and would therefore be expected to remove the glasses when looking at distant objects.

Exercise 2.3B

1 An optometrist discovers that her patient can clearly see objects at distances between 25 cm and 200 cm from his eye.

(a) From what defect of vision is the patient suffering?

(b) What spectacles are required to enable the patient to clearly see very distant objects?

(c) Calculate the power of the spectacle lens which would be prescribed.

(d) What is the patient's range of vision when using these spectacles?

2 A person's far point is at infinity, but he cannot clearly see objects closer than 150 cm from his eye.

(a) Draw a diagram to illustrate what happens at the retina when this person is looking at an object less than 150 cm from his eye.

(b) What name is given to this defect of vision?

(c) What type of spectacle lens is required to reduce his least distance of distinct vision from 150 cm to 25 cm?

(d) Calculate the focal length of this lens.

3 An elderly woman with failing vision cannot see objects closer than 70 cm and further away than 500 cm.

(a) What spectacle lens would be prescribed to give this patient the ability to clearly see objects at a distance of 25 cm from her eyes?

(b) What would be her range of vision with this lens?

(c) What spectacle lens would be prescribed to give this patient the ability to clearly see objects at an infinite distance from her eyes?

(d) What would be the patient's range of vision with this lens?

4 The distance between a man's eye lens and his retina is 18 mm. He focuses on an object of height 60 cm at a distance of 72 cm from his eye.

What is the height of the image on his retina?

2.4 Superposition, Interference and Diffraction

You should be able to:

2.4.1 Illustrate the concept of superposition by the graphical addition of two sinusoidal waves

2.4.2 Demonstrate an understanding of the conditions required to produce standing waves

2.4.3 Demonstrate knowledge and understanding of the graphical representation of standing waves in stretched strings and in air in pipes closed at one end

2.4.4 Identify, graphically, the modes of vibration of stretched strings and air in a pipe closed at one end, without reference to overtone and harmonic terminology

2.4.5 Identify node and antinode positions

2.4.6 Perform and describe an experiment to measure the speed of sound in air using a resonance tube (end correction is not required)

2.4.7 Demonstrate an understanding of the conditions for observable interference

2.4.8 Demonstrate an understanding of the significance of path difference and phase difference in explaining interference effects

2.4.9 Describe Young's slits interference experiment to measure the wavelength of monochromatic light

2.4.10 Use the equation $\lambda = \dfrac{a\,y}{d}$ ⟵ *y = fringe separation*

2.4.11 Describe and explain diffraction phenomena at a single slit

2.4.12 State qualitatively and draw diagrams to illustrate the effect of aperture size on diffraction

2.4.13 Use the equation $d \sin \theta = n\lambda$ for a diffraction grating

2.4.14 Describe the use of a diffraction grating and a laser to measure wavelength.

Principle of Superposition

NODE – position within spatial interference pattern where amplitude is at a minimum. (opposite for anti-node)

The Principle of Superposition may be applied to waves whenever two (or more) waves travelling through the same medium at the same time meet. The waves pass through each other without being disturbed.

Nodes → fixed ends

The Principle of Superposition states that the resultant displacement of the medium at any point in space is the sum of the displacements that each wave would cause at that point at that time.

Anti-nodes → open ends

Remember that displacement is a vector, so direction is important when we apply the Principle of Superposition.

in phase

When two waves overlap in phase they produce a wave of greater amplitude. At a certain point in space the crests of each wave coincide exactly (as do the troughs) and therefore a wave with <u>greater amplitude</u> is produced. This is known as **constructive interference**.

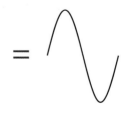

Anti-nodes

Consider one wave & helps the other, e.g. double height

path difference is even no. of ½ wavelengths

nodes — *think 'no displacement'*

anti-phase

However, when the crest of one wave coincides with the trough of the other wave the displacements of the two waves are in opposite directions. If the amplitudes are equal then they cancel each other. This is called **total destructive interference**.

path difference is odd no. of ½ wavelengths

✱ same f required

If the amplitudes are not the same then when destructive interference takes place the resultant wave has a smaller amplitude. This time the two waves do not completely cancel.

Remember that the Principle of Superposition applies to all situations when two or more waves meet. To find the resultant displacement of two waves at any instant or any point represented, we apply the Principle of Superposition by adding their individual displacements at that instant or point to find the resultant displacement at that instant or point.

sources coherent if constant phase difference with time.

Worked examples

Two electromagnetic waves, W_1 and W_2, with the same amplitude come together in time and space at a point P. W_2 has twice the period of W_1. At time $t = 0$ both waves have zero displacement, and then both displacements increase in the same direction.

The graph below shows how displacement varies with time for wave W_1, at the point P.

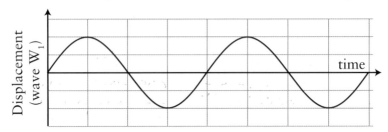

1   Make two copies of the grid above and draw:

   (a) the displacement-time graph for wave W_2.

   (b) the displacement-time graph for the resultant wave produced by the superposition of W_1 and W_2.

Solution

(a)

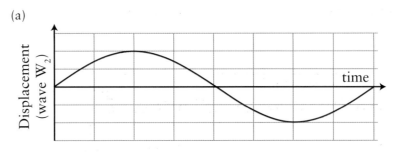

Wave W_2 has the same amplitude as wave W_1. Since its frequency is only half that of W_1, only one complete wave will fit into the time represented along the x-axis.

Only get perfect nodes when amplitudes are the same

perfect nodes when amplitudes are the Similar amplitudes for observable interference for max. contrast.

(b)

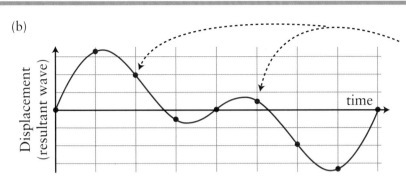

Displacement (resultant wave)

time

To draw the resultant wave the displacement of W_1 is added to the displacement of W_2 at each instant. The resultant is shown by the dots.

When the dots are joined the shape of the resultant wave is obtained.

2 The frequency of wave W_1 is 4×10^{15} Hz.

(a) What is the frequency of wave W_2?

(b) What is the frequency of the resultant wave produced by the superposition of W_1 and W_2?

Solution

(a) The period of W_2 is twice that of W_1. Since $f = \dfrac{1}{T}$, the frequency of wave W_2 is half that of W_1. So the frequency of W_2 is $\frac{1}{2}\,(4 \times 10^{15}) = 2 \times 10^{15}$ Hz.

(b) Although the waveform of the resultant wave is more complex, the time between successive repetitions (period) is the same for it and W_2. Therefore the frequency of the resultant wave is also 2×10^{15} Hz.

Standing waves

These are sometimes called **stationary waves**. They are produced by the interference of two waves, of the same type and having the same wavelength and speed, but moving in opposite directions. The most common occurrence of this is a wave travelling in one direction meeting its reflection which is moving in the opposite direction.

The distance between a node + anti-node in a standing wave is ¼ wavelength.

The Principle of Superposition can be used to explain and describe what is seen when the outgoing wave and its reflection meet.

Melde's apparatus, shown below, can be used to show standing waves. The vibration generator vibrates up and down, driven by a signal generator (a source of alternating voltage whose frequency can be altered). The vibration generator moves up and down with a small amplitude and this causes waves to travel along the string.

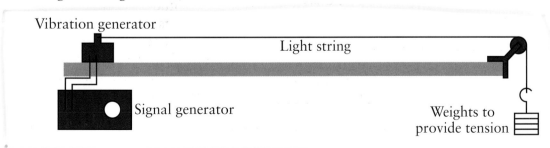

Vibration generator

Light string

Signal generator

Weights to provide tension

When the waves meet the pulley end of the string they are reflected back along the string. So we have two waves of the same wavelength moving in opposite directions. The result is a **standing wave**.

The simplest pattern and the lowest frequency at which the string vibrates is called the fundamental frequency, f_1. The diagram below shows the standing wave pattern obtained as the frequency of vibration is increased. The relationship between these modes of vibration can be deduced using the wave equation. The length of the string is L and the speed of the waves on the string is v. The letters N and A stand for Node and Antinode, discussed in more detail on page 130.

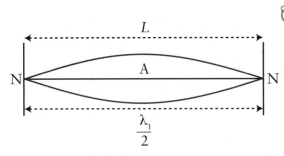

Off syllabus

Fundamental 1st mode $f_0 = \dfrac{v}{2L}$

Frequency = f_1 and Wavelength $\lambda_1 = 2L$

$$v = f_1\lambda_1 \quad f_1 = \frac{v}{\lambda_1} = \frac{v}{2L}$$

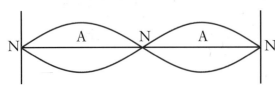

2nd Next mode of vibration $f_1 = 2\left(\dfrac{v}{2L}\right)$

Frequency = f_2 and $\lambda_2 = L$

$$v = f_2\lambda_2 \quad f_2 = \frac{v}{\lambda_2} = \frac{v}{L} = 2f_1$$

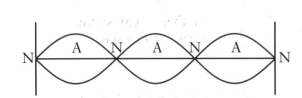

3rd Next mode of vibration $f_2 = 3\left(\dfrac{v}{3L}\right)$

Frequency = f_3 and $\lambda_3 = \dfrac{2L}{3}$

$$v = f_3\lambda_3 \quad f_3 = \frac{v}{\lambda_3} = \frac{3v}{2L} = 3f_1$$

$$f = \frac{v}{\lambda}$$

Observe that the frequency, f_n, of the nth mode of vibration is $\dfrac{nv}{2L}$.

To explain the formation of a standing wave we have to apply the Principle of Superposition to the wave travelling out from the source and its reflected wave. In the diagrams on the next page, the outgoing wave is shown as the dotted line (··········) and is moving to the right. The reflected wave is the dashed line (·----˗) and is moving to the left. The standing wave is the resultant of these two waves and is shown by the solid line (⌒).

In each case, the incident wave is shown in steps of $\dfrac{\lambda}{8}$ as it moves to the right and the reflected waves in steps of $\dfrac{\lambda}{8}$ as it moves to the left. T is the period of the waves, i.e. the time it takes for one complete wave to pass a point.

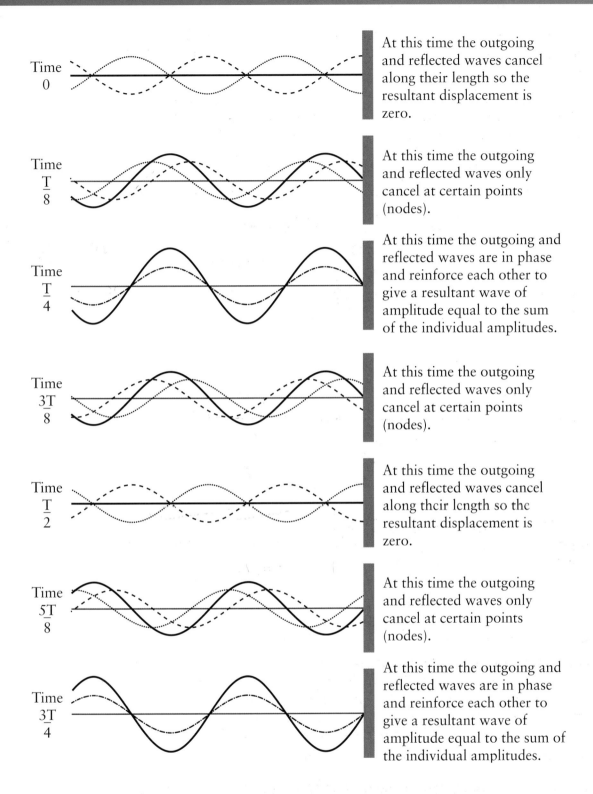

Time 0 — At this time the outgoing and reflected waves cancel along their length so the resultant displacement is zero.

Time $\frac{T}{8}$ — At this time the outgoing and reflected waves only cancel at certain points (nodes).

Time $\frac{T}{4}$ — At this time the outgoing and reflected waves are in phase and reinforce each other to give a resultant wave of amplitude equal to the sum of the individual amplitudes.

Time $\frac{3T}{8}$ — At this time the outgoing and reflected waves only cancel at certain points (nodes).

Time $\frac{T}{2}$ — At this time the outgoing and reflected waves cancel along their length so the resultant displacement is zero.

Time $\frac{5T}{8}$ — At this time the outgoing and reflected waves only cancel at certain points (nodes).

Time $\frac{3T}{4}$ — At this time the outgoing and reflected waves are in phase and reinforce each other to give a resultant wave of amplitude equal to the sum of the individual amplitudes.

Note: the wavelength of the standing wave is equal to the wavelength of the progressive waves from which it is formed.

Nodes and antinodes

When a standing or stationary wave is created, some points along the wave are always at rest, i.e. their resultant displacement is always zero. These points are known as **nodes**.

Between the nodes all the points are vibrating, i.e. the amplitude of vibration varies. Midway between two nodal points the amplitude of vibration is a maximum. This point is called an **antinode**.

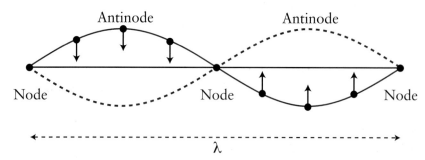

(handwritten note) λ goes up by 0.5 for every mode e.g. ½λ → 1λ → 3/2 λ

For standing waves on strings between two fixed points you must remember:

- Standing waves are formed when two waves of the same wavelength and frequency, but travelling in opposite directions, come together in time and space and superpose.

- There is always a node at the fixed points.

- The points between neighbouring nodes are vibrating in phase with each other.

- The points between the next pair of nodes are vibrating ½λ out of phase with corresponding points between the previous pair of nodes, as shown in the diagram above.

- The distance between neighbouring nodes is ½λ.

- The distance between a node and the nearest antinode is ¼λ.

- The wavelength and frequency are different for different modes of vibration, but the speed is the same.

Standing waves in air columns

Standing waves can be demonstrated with sound using a long glass tube closed at one end. This is commonly known as a **resonance tube**. Sound waves are generated at the top of the air column using a loudspeaker or tuning fork. Sound waves from the speaker or tuning fork meet the reflected waves from the bottom of the air column and a standing wave is created.

When a standing wave is produced the sound becomes much louder. This is easily checked by removing the glass tube. If a standing wave was present there should be a very noticeable decrease in the loudness of the sound.

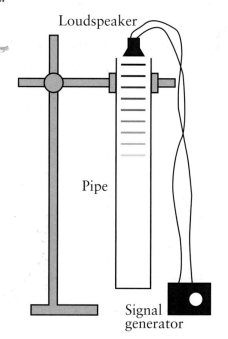

The lowest frequency of sound which creates a standing wave for a particular length of air column is called the ~~fundamental.~~ *first mode.*

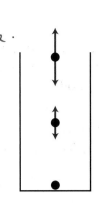

The diagram on the right shows three air molecules at three different positions along the air column in the glass tube. Sound is a longitudinal wave so the vibrations are along the length of the air column, parallel to the direction of propagation of the sound wave.

The air molecule at the closed end is not vibrating: this is a **node**. The air molecule at the open end is vibrating with maximum amplitude: this is an **antinode**.

The air molecule further down the pipe is vibrating with an amplitude less than that of the molecule at the open end. As we move from the node to the antinode, the amplitude of vibration of the air molecules increases.

One way to represent a wave is a graph showing how the displacement of the particles varies with distance along the tube. When this is done for the fundamental mode of vibration of the air in the column, we have the graph shown on the right.

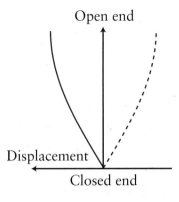

The displacement of the particles gradually increases from the closed end to the open end.

The dotted line represents the displacement of the particles half a period later.

Fixed length of air column – varying frequency

$$V = 4fl \quad \text{for speed of sound.}$$

As shown on the left (page 130), a small loudspeaker connected to a signal generator can be used to create standing waves in an air column of fixed length. As the frequency is gradually increased, the loudness of the sound noticeably increases (resonates) at certain frequencies. At each of these frequencies a standing wave is created and these are known as modes of vibration.

The lowest frequency is called the fundamental; the next frequency at which a standing wave is created is known as the first overtone; the next frequency is known as the second overtone. But note that the specification does not require candidates to use overtone or harmonics terminology.

old spec → *this terminology is NOT used.*

The diagram below shows the standing wave patterns for the four lowest frequencies for which a standing wave is created in an air column of fixed length.

$L = \dfrac{\lambda}{4}$

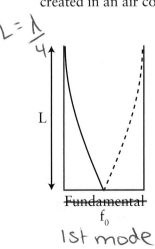

Fundamental
f_0

1st mode
f_1

$L = \dfrac{3}{4}\lambda$

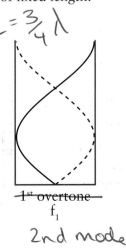

1st overtone
f_1

2nd mode
f_2

$L = \dfrac{5}{4}\lambda$

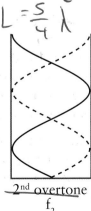

2nd overtone
f_2

odd no. of ¼ wavelengths only.

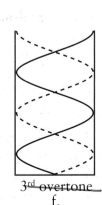

3rd overtone
f_3

The node is never centred.

Fixed frequency – varying length of air column

It is also possible to use a single tuning fork of fixed frequency and instead increase the length of the air column, using the apparatus below. If fundamental resonance occurs at length L, then the next highest mode of vibration occurs at length $3L$, the next highest at $5L$ and so on.

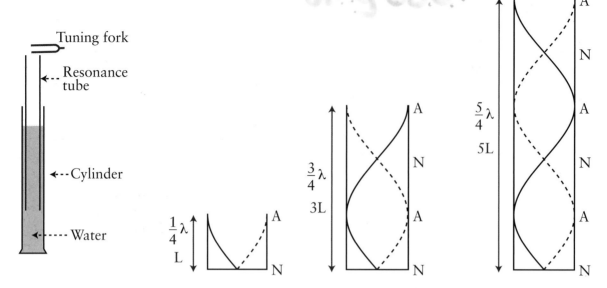

Measuring the speed of sound

Standing waves of sound in air provides a method of measuring the speed of sound in air.

Method 1 Using the fundamental mode

In this approach tuning forks of known frequencies are used to create standing waves. The tuning fork is made to vibrate and then held over the open end of a glass tube as shown above.

The glass tube is raised or lowered until the fundamental mode of vibration is produced. This is the shortest length of the air column at which the sound becomes noticeably louder. The length of the air column is measured.

This procedure is repeated for a number of tuning forks of different frequencies.

If you refer back to the previous chapter, you will recall that in the fundamental mode of vibration the length of the air column L is ¼ of the wavelength of the sound.

Using this fact in the wave equation gives:

$$v = f\lambda \text{ and } \lambda = 4L$$

so: $v = 4Lf$

so: $L = \dfrac{v}{4f} = \dfrac{v}{4} \times \dfrac{1}{f}$

The equation of a straight line passing through the origin is:

$$y = mx$$

So, a graph of L (y-axis) against $\dfrac{1}{f}$ (x-axis) yields a straight line.

The gradient of this line equals $\frac{v}{4}$. The measurements and graph from such an experiment are shown below.

Frequency of the tuning fork f / Hz	Length of the Air column L / m	$\frac{1}{f}$ / Hz^{-1}
512	0.165	1.95×10^{-3}
480	0.180	2.08×10^{-3}
362	0.235	2.76×10^{-3}
304	0.280	3.29×10^{-3}
256	0.335	3.91×10^{-3}

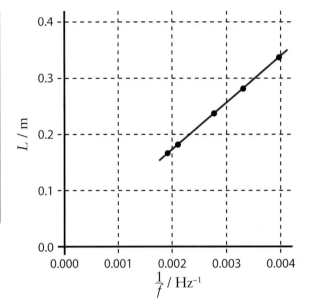

These measurements give a gradient of 86 m s^{-1} so the speed of sound obtained is 344 m s^{-1}.

Method 2 Using the first and second positions of resonance

In this method one frequency is used. The fundamental mode of vibration is first found. This is the shortest length of the air column at which a loud sound is heard. The length L_1 of the air column is measured. This is also known as the first position of resonance. Using the same frequency the next shortest length at which a loud sound is heard is found. This is the second position of resonance. The new length L_2 of the air column is measured.

$$L_1 = \tfrac{1}{4}\lambda \quad \text{and} \quad L_2 = \tfrac{3}{4}\lambda \quad \text{so:} \quad L_2 - L_1 = \tfrac{1}{2}\lambda$$

Using the wave equation $v = f\lambda$, the velocity v can be found since the frequency f is known. This method should be repeated for a number of frequencies and an average value for the velocity of sound calculated.

Exercise 2.4A

1 The graph on the right shows two waves. One has a period of 40 ms and the other has a period of 80 ms. One has an amplitude of 2 cm and the other has an amplitude of 1 cm.

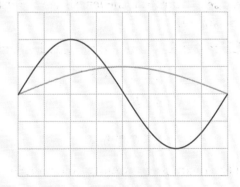

(a) Make a copy of the graph. Label the vertical and horizontal axes and write on each the appropriate numbers to illustrate the scale.

(b) Use the Principle of Superposition to draw the resultant waveform.

(c) State the frequency of the resultant waveform.

2 (a) What are the main differences between a stationary wave and a progressive wave?

(b) What are the necessary conditions to produce a standing wave?

(c) In the context of standing waves, what do physicists mean by the words node and antinode?

3 A loudspeaker, connected to a signal generator, is placed close to the open end of a resonance tube, closed at the opposite end. The frequency of the signal generator is increased slowly from an initially low value until the first position of resonance is obtained.

(a) How would the experimentalist know when resonance was taking place?

(b) Why is it important to increase the frequency slowly from an initially low value?

(c) (i) Make a copy of the diagram below. Illustrate the mode of vibration at the first position of resonance and label the node (N) and the antinode (A).

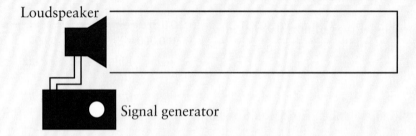

The tube is 30 cm long and the frequency of the note at the first position of resonance is 280 Hz.

(ii) Calculate the wavelength of the standing wave in the tube at the first position of resonance.

(iii) Use your answer to part (ii) to calculate the speed of the standing wave in the tube.

The air in the tube is now replaced with gas, G, in which sound travels at 420 m s⁻¹.

(iv) Calculate the frequency at which the second position of resonance will be found in this resonance tube.

4 An experiment is carried out on standing waves using the apparatus shown in the diagram below. The frequency of the vibration generator is adjusted until fundamental resonance is observed on the string. The distance between the vibration generator and the pulley, L, is then reduced and the new fundamental frequency is found. The speed of the waves on the string is constant.

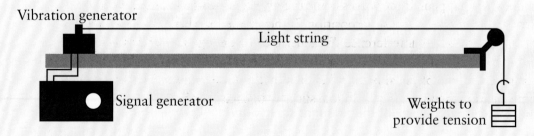

The results of this investigation are recorded as in the table below.

Length, L / cm	100	120	140	160	180	200
Fundamental frequency, f / Hz	36.0	30.0	25.7	22.5	20.0	18.0

(a) Show that the relationship between f and L is $f = \dfrac{v}{2L}$, where v is the speed of the standing wave on the string.

(b) What straight line graph should you plot to find the speed of the standing waves?

(c) Plot this graph and determine its gradient to two significant figures. Remember to give the unit.

(d) Use your answer to (c) to find the speed of the standing waves on the string to two significant figures.

(e) A student claims the graph you have drawn proves the fundamental frequency of the waves on the string is directly proportional to the length, L. Do you agree? Give a reason for your answer.

Interference of sound waves

S_1 and S_2 are two speakers. To achieve coherent sources of sound, the same signal generator powers each speaker, so that they produce sound waves of the same frequency and in phase. As the sound waves from each speaker spread out they cross. This creates places where the sound is loud (constructive interference) and between these there are places where the sound is soft (destructive interference).

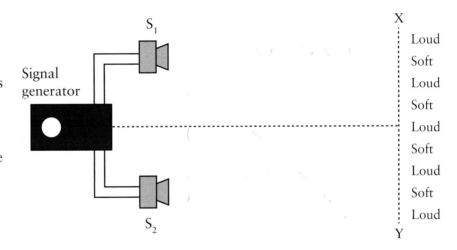

If you were to walk along the line XY you would hear these alternate loud and soft sounds.

Why does this happen? If the waves come together 'crest-to-crest', then we have constructive interference by superposition. If they come together 'crest-to-trough', then we get destructive interference. Whether they come together 'crest-to-crest' or 'crest-to-trough' depends on the path difference. The path difference is simply the difference in the physical paths taken by the interfering waves. This will become clearer when we discuss double slit interference in light.

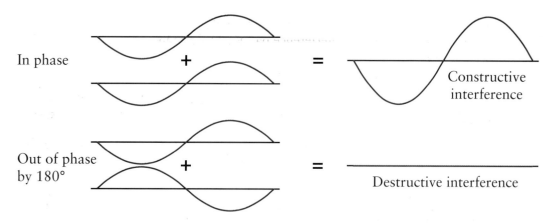

In phase   +   =   Constructive interference

Out of phase by 180°   +   =   Destructive interference

Coherence

To produce an interference pattern that is detectable, i.e. lasts long enough to be seen or heard, the two sources of waves must be **coherent**.

To be coherent the sources must produce waves of the same wavelength or frequency and be in phase, i.e. each produces a wave crest at the same time, or have a constant phase difference between them.

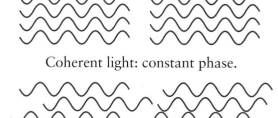

Coherent light: constant phase.

Incoherent light: random stream of energy bursts.

Light waves from an incandescent (hot filament) source are generally emitted with a wide range of wavelengths and therefore cannot be coherent. However, even if we were to look at the light of a particular wavelength within the beam, this light is not coherent either. This is because the light is emitted as a random stream of energy bursts. In practice, schools often find it most convenient to **use laser light as a coherent source**. Where a laser is not used, **the light must originate from a single source.**

Sound from two different tuning forks are similarly incoherent. However, sound from two loud speakers powered by the same signal generator would be coherent.

To make the contrast between constructive and destructive interference more obvious, it is very desirable that the coherent sources are of equal amplitude. However, **equal amplitude is not a requirement for coherence.**

Young's double slit experiment with laser light

Light from a laser is used to illuminate two narrow slits. The light from a laser is coherent so each slit then acts as a coherent source of light waves. The light waves spread out as they pass through the slits. This effect is known as diffraction.

At points on the screen the light waves from each slit interfere constructively and a bright line is seen. In between the bright regions there are dark regions where destructive interference is occurring. On the screen alternate bright and dark regions are seen. These are often referred to as **interference fringes**. Because the fringes can be quite dim, it is desirable to carry out this experiment in a darkened room.

In the diagram on the right, S_1 and S_2 are two coherent sources of light, of wavelength λ, separated by a distance, a. An interference pattern of alternate bright and dark fringes is seen on the screen. The separation of bright fringes is y. The distance from the double slit to the screen is d.

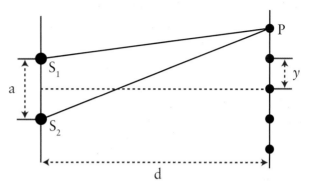

The point P is the location of a bright fringe. The waves reaching P from S_1 and S_2 have travelled different distances. If a whole number of wavelengths can fit into this path difference then constructive interference results since a crest from S_1 will arrive at the same time as a crest from S_2.

For constructive interference path difference $S_2P - S_1P = n\lambda$

If a whole number plus half a wavelength fits into the path difference, destructive interference results.

For destructive interference path difference $S_2P - S_1P = (n + \frac{1}{2})\lambda$

In each of these conditions n has the value 0, 1, 2, 3, … i.e. whole numbers.

Consider now waves interfering at a distance y from the axis of symmetry. It can be shown mathematically (no physics involved) that the path difference between the waves interfering here is given by $\frac{ay}{d}$. So, if this is the first point above the axis of symmetry where constructive interference occurs, then:

$$\text{Path difference} = \frac{ay}{d} = n\lambda$$

and here $n = 1$ because it is the first bright fringe above the axis of symmetry.

Hence: $\lambda = \frac{ay}{d}$ where λ = wavelength of the light in m
a = separation of the double slits in m
y = fringe separation on the screen in m
d = distance from the double slit to the screen in m

The distance from the double slit to the screen d can be measured using a metre rule. This distance is typically 1–2 m. The fringe separation y is best found by measuring the separation of a number of fringes and taking an average.

The manufacturer often gives the separation of the two slits in the double slit arrangement. Alternatively, it can be found by projecting a magnified image on to a screen, and measuring their separation on this magnified image. The actual magnification can be found by projecting a transparent millimetre scale onto the same screen. The actual separation of the two slits is then found by dividing their separation on the magnified image by the magnification.

The separation of the slits is typically 0.2 mm.

Young's original double slit experiment

Young carried out his original double slit experiment with light in the first decade of the 1800s and, of course, he had no access to a laser. So how did he get coherent light?

In the original double slit experiment, the white light first passes through a filter to produce **monochromatic light** (single wavelength). It then passes through a narrow single slit and as it does so it diffracts (the waves spread out). Finally the waves pass through the double slit, the crest of one wave passing through each one of the double slits at the same time. These two actions ensure that the two slits S_1 and S_2 act as coherent sources of light waves.

The waves of light from the two slits interfered to produce a characteristic fringe pattern on a screen, the first piece of direct evidence for the wave nature of light.

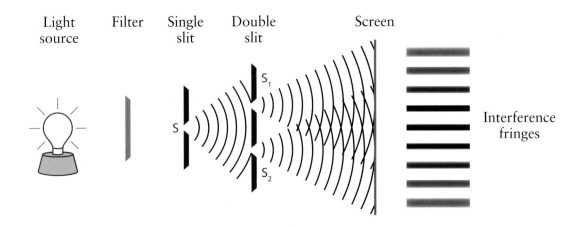

Exercise 2.4B

1 (a) In the context of the superposition of two light waves, what condition must exist for maximum constructive interference?

   (b) How would you recognise that maximum constructive interference has occurred?

2 (a) What is meant by (i) monochromatic light and (ii) coherent light?

   (b) Why can light coming from two different candle flames never give an observable interference pattern?

   (c) Why was it necessary for Young to have a single slit in front of his double slit to obtain an observable interference pattern?

3 In a Young double slit experiment a pair of slits, 400 µm apart, were placed 2.4 m from a screen. Monochromatic light fell incident on the double slit and fringes were observed. The distance from the axis of symmetry to the centre of the tenth bright fringe was 30 mm.

   (a) Calculate the wavelength of the monochromatic light.

   (b) Calculate the distance from the axis of symmetry to the centre of the tenth bright fringe if the slit separation had been 200 µm and the slit screen distance had been 1.2 m.

4   In an experiment to measure the speed of sound in air, two loudspeakers, S_1 and S_2, connected to the same signal generator are placed 0.30 m apart. The signal generator is set to 8000 Hz. Sound intensity measurements are made along a line 1.2 m from the speakers, perpendicular to the axis of symmetry.

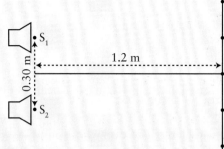

At certain points, marked with large dots on the diagram on the right, the sound intensity was at a maximum.

(a) Why was it necessary to connect the speakers to the same signal generator if points of maximum sound intensity were to be obtained?

(b) Explain why a sound intensity maximum was obtained on the axis of symmetry.

(c) Draw a copy of the diagram and mark with the letter P the point at which the path difference $S_1P - S_2P$ is equal to the wavelength of the sound.

The distance between the second intensity maximum above the axis of symmetry and the second intensity maximum below the axis of symmetry was 0.60 m.

(d) Calculate (i) the wavelength and (ii) the speed of the sound emitted from the speakers.

5   (a) Explain why it is not possible to obtain an observable interference pattern with Young's double slit apparatus using two separate light sources.

(b) In a Young's double slit experiment using light of wavelength 500 nm, the separation of the fringes was observed to be 1.5 mm. What would be the effect on the fringe separation of the following:

(i) doubling the distance between the screen and the double slit?

(ii) doubling the distance between the two slits?

(c) Explain why Young's interference fringes cannot be seen with light of wavelength 1000 nm.

6   You watch a Young's double slit interference experiment in a school laboratory. The light source is a helium-neon laser which emits light with a wavelength around 630 nm.

(a) Why is a single slit before the double slits not necessary with the laser, but essential with monochromatic sodium light?

The fringes are not far enough apart, so your teacher moves the laser and double slits further away from the screen. The observed fringes are now bright and well separated.

(b) What problem might there be if the teacher tried to do the same thing with monochromatic sodium light?

Diffraction and aperture size at a single slit

As waves go through a gap they spread out. This is called **diffraction**. Diffraction also takes place when waves meet any type of obstacle. A suitable definition of diffraction is the changing of direction of waves to bend around corners and spread out as they encounter obstacles.

The diagrams on the right show how the diffraction increases as the size of the gap is gradually decreased until is about the same size as the wavelength of the incident wave. The greatest diffraction happens when the size of the gap is about the same as the wavelength of the wave.

The wavelength of the wave does **not** change as a result of diffraction.

The wavelength of everyday sounds is about the same width as a door. As a result diffraction of sound at an open door results in sound waves spreading into the room, allowing us to hear sounds coming along a corridor. Light has a much smaller wavelength so very narrow openings or slits are required to observe diffraction of light.

A laser and an adjustable slit can be used to investigate the diffraction of light. The laser beam is directed through the slit and onto a screen as shown in the diagram below.

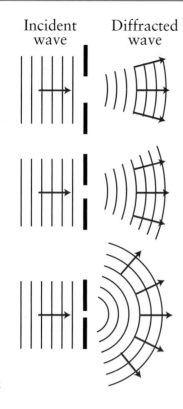

Incident wave   Diffracted wave

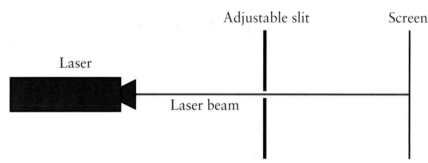

Laser   Adjustable slit   Screen

Laser beam

Diffraction of the light waves at a **single slit** produces a diffraction pattern like that shown opposite. As the light waves spread out in some directions destructive interference occurs, producing the dark bands. In other directions constructive interference occurs, producing the bright bands.

Most of the energy of the light waves passes through in a narrow region giving rise to the bright central maximum. The width of the central maximum depends on the width of the slit and on the wavelength of the light used.

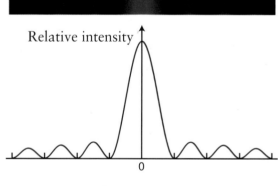

Diffraction pattern observed

Relative intensity

0

For the same slit width, blue light has a narrower diffraction pattern than red light because the wavelength of blue is less than the wavelength of red.

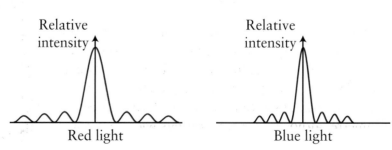

Relative intensity   Relative intensity

Red light   Blue light

As the width of the slit decreases:

- the width of the diffraction pattern increases (so fewer maxima are observed)
- the heights of the maxima decrease (because less energy arrives on the screen)

Small slit width · · · · · · · · · · · · · · · · · · · Large slit width

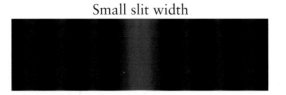

Note, compared to the subsidiary maxima the central maximum is:
- many times more intense
- twice the width

Angle of diffraction and the minima

Suppose a parallel beam of monochromatic, coherent light falls upon a small single slit. The beam diffracts in different directions but we will just concentrate on one direction towards a point P in a direction θ to the original direction of the waves. Plane waves arrive at P due to diffraction at the slit AB. Waves coming from the two sides of the slit have a path difference BN and therefore interference results.

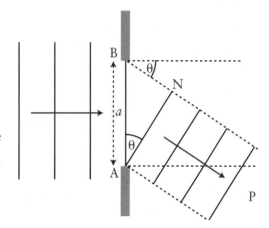

If this path difference is equal to the wavelength of the light (λ), the light from the top of the slit and the bottom of the slit will cancel out and a minimum is observed at P. This is because if the path difference between the two extremes of the slit is exactly one wavelength, for every point in the upper half of the slit there is a corresponding point in the lower half for which the rays reaching P are exactly half a wavelength out of phase.

The angle between the axis of symmetry and the direction of the diffracted light is called the angle of diffraction, θ. The central maximum is called order zero, the first maximum above (or below) the central maximum is called order 1, the second maximum is order 2 and so on. Diffraction order is given the symbol n.

It can be shown that for a single slit of width a, diffracting light of wavelength λ, the relationship for n^{th} **minimum** is:

$n\lambda = a \sin \theta$

The diffraction grating formula

A grating is a rectangular piece of glass treated on one side to make it opaque and then scored on the opaque side to produce parallel lines of equal width and equal separation. Using this method it is possible to obtain diffraction gratings with as many as 3000 lines per millimetre, although 'coarse' gratings with between

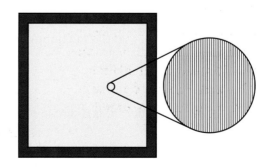

80 and 300 lines per millimetre are more common in schools. The glass grating is then mounted on a slide.

If light of a single wavelength, such as that from a laser, is used, then a series of sharp lines occur, one line to each order of the spectrum.

With a white light source a series of spectra is formed. The central fringe is white because all colours from red to violet are diffracted to that point. On either side of the central fringe are spectra, with the light of the shortest wavelength having the smallest angle of diffraction.

We will be considering transmission gratings only – the light is diffracted as it passes through the scored lines of the grating.

Consider a parallel beam of light incident normally on a diffraction grating with a grating element d (the grating element is the inverse of the number of lines per unit length). Consider light that is diffracted at an angle θ to the normal and coming from corresponding points on adjacent slits. So the angle of diffraction, θ, marked on the diagram is also equal to the angle ABC.

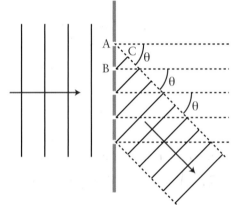

For a maximum, the path difference = AC = $n\lambda$

The grating element, d = AB

So, AC = $d \sin \theta$

Therefore **for a maximum:**

$d \sin \theta = n\lambda$

where the diffraction order n = 0, 1, 2, 3...

Worked Example

1 A helium-neon laser illuminates normally a diffraction grating with 250 lines per millimetre. The angular separation of the first order lines is 18.2°.

(a) Calculate the size of the grating element, d.
(b) Calculate the angle of diffraction, θ, in the first order.
(c) Calculate the wavelength of laser light.
(d) Calculate the highest order possible with the grating when using this laser.

Solution

(a) $d = \dfrac{1}{N} = \dfrac{1}{250} = 0.004$ mm $= 4\times10^{-6}$ m   (b) $\theta = \dfrac{18.2°}{2} = 9.1°$

(c) $d \sin \theta = n\lambda$, and here $n = 1$, because we are dealing with the first order.

$4\times10^{-6} \sin 9.1° = \lambda = 633$ nm

(d) $n = \dfrac{d \sin \theta}{\lambda}$, so the maximum value of n occurs when $\sin \theta$ is a maximum.

$n_{max} = \dfrac{d}{\lambda} = \dfrac{4\times10^{-6}}{633\times10^{-9}} = 6.32$

But the order, n, is a whole number, so:

$n_{max} = 6$

Using a diffraction grating to find the wavelength of light from a laser

A laser provides an intense beam of monochromatic, coherent light. To find the wavelength of the light we use a diffraction grating of known grating element, d, a large screen and a metre rule.

Method

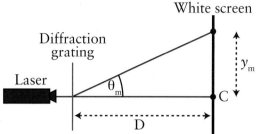

- Place a helium-neon laser on a bench and a large white screen in front of it, at least 1 m away.
- Switch on the laser and mark the spot on the white screen. This is the point C on the diagram.
- Switch off the laser and mount the grating with the lines running vertically about 10 cm in front of the laser.
- Measure the distance between the grating and the screen with a metre stick. This is the distance D.
- Switch the laser on once more.
- Immediately observable is a series of diffraction lines on the screen, similar to that shown opposite.

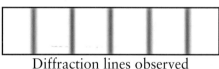

Diffraction lines observed

- Measure, with a ruler, the distance y_n between C and the nth bright fringe for values of nth from (say) $n = 1$ to $n = 5$.
- Calculate the angle θ_n, given by $\theta_n = \tan^{-1}\left(\dfrac{y_n}{D}\right)$.
- Record the results in a table, like that below.

Order, n	1	2	3	4	5
y_n / mm	160	334	539	818	1290
angle θ_n / °	9.1	18.4	28.3	39.3	52.3
$\sin(\theta_n)$	0.158	0.316	0.474	0.633	0.791

- Plot the graph of $d.\sin\theta$ against n. (d, the grating element, is given by the manufacturer.)
- Since $d.\sin\theta = n\lambda$, the wavelength, λ, is the gradient of this graph.

Precautions when using a laser

1 Never look directly into any laser beam, regardless of its power.
2 The outside of the lab door should have a notice pinned to it reading 'LASER IN USE – DO NOT ENTER'.
3 Remove all unnecessary, shiny, reflecting surfaces from the work area. This will prevent any undesirable reflections causing laser light to enter the eyes.
4 As far as possible, work with normal room light. This will keep the pupils of your eyes from becoming any larger than necessary. The larger the pupil, the easier it is to damage the retina.
5 Any accident involving laser light should be reported immediately to the teacher in charge and, where appropriate, a medical opinion should be obtained.

Exercise 2.4C

1 A band is marching down a street towards a road junction. There are tall buildings all around. The drummers produce high wavelength sound and the trombonists produce low wavelength sound. Which sound is the observer likely to hear first? Give a reason for your answer.

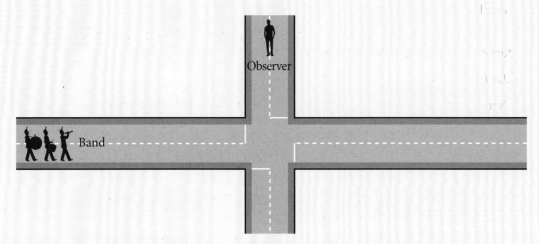

2 (a) What is diffraction?

(b) A manufacturer produces a diffraction grating with 250 slits per millimetre of its width.

(i) Show that the distance between the centres of neighbouring slits is 4 µm.

(ii) A laser beam is incident normally at the grating. The first order beams leave the grating at angles of 9.1° either side of the grating normal. Calculate the wavelength of the laser light.

(iii) Calculate the angle between the third order beams.

(iv) What is the highest order of the diffracted light which can be produced with this diffraction grating and this laser?

3 A lamp emits light of wavelengths 668 nm and 587 nm. The light is incident on a diffraction grating with grating element 2 µm.

Calculate the angular separation of these lines in the second order spectrum.

4 The third order violet spectrum (λ = 400 nm) overlaps with the second order orange spectrum when using a particular diffraction grating. If the grating has an element of 4 µm, calculate:

(a) the angular separation of violet light in the third order.

(b) the wavelength of the orange light.

2.5 Quantum Physics

You should be able to:

2.5.1   Recall and use the equation $E_{photon} = hf$

2.5.2   Use the photon model to explain the photoelectric effect qualitatively using the terms photon energy and work function

2.5.3   Use the equation $\frac{1}{2} mv_{max}^2 = hf - hf_o$

2.5.4   Demonstrate an understanding that electrons exist in energy levels in atoms

2.5.5   Recall and use the equation $hf = \Delta E$

2.5.6   Provide a simple explanation of laser action, using the terms population inversion and metastable state

2.5.7   Demonstrate an understanding of the production of X-rays by the process of electron movement between energy levels

2.5.8   Describe the physical principles of CT scanning and conventional X-rays

Photon model and the photoelectric effect

The photoelectric effect occurs when electrons are ejected from the surface of a metal when electromagnetic radiation of sufficiently high frequency falls on it. The electrons emitted by this process are called **photoelectrons**. The effect was first discovered by Heinrich Hertz in 1887. However, a full explanation was not given until Albert Einstein published his famous paper in 1905. It was for his explanation of the photoelectric effect that Einstein was later to receive his Nobel Prize.

The effect can be readily demonstrated with a gold leaf electroscope. The experiment uses the fact that zinc metal emits electrons when exposed to ultraviolet light.

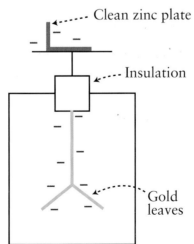

Clean zinc plate

Insulation

Gold leaves

E.M. waves come to metal surface, resulting in release of electrons

When the electroscope is negatively charged, by momentarily connecting the metal cap of the electroscope to the negative terminal of a high voltage supply (for example, 300 V), the leaves diverge due to the electrostatic repulsion between them.

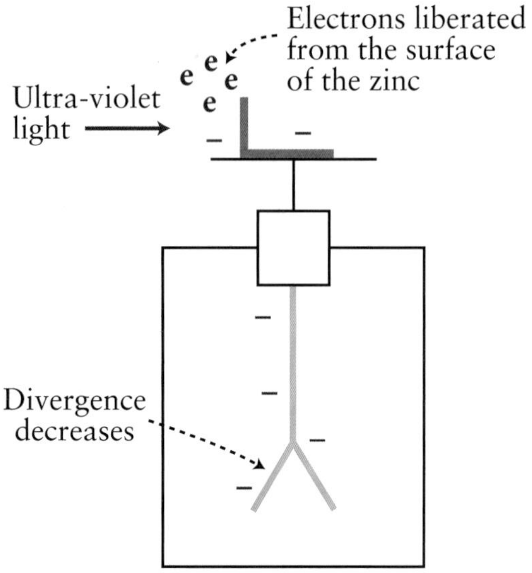

The clean zinc strip is then illuminated with ultraviolet light, and it is observed that the divergence of the leaves becomes less. The zinc is losing electrons due to the ultra-violet light, so the excess of electrons that we started off with is decreasing.

A sheet of glass inserted between the source of the ultra-violet light and the zinc will stop this collapse of the leaves. Glass absorbs ultra-violet light. When the glass is removed the collapse of the leaves continues.

Instantaneous release. Time is no factor.

Brighter light emits more due to more photons.

To explain interference of light we used wave theory. Wave theory considered radiation to be emitted continuously in waves. To explain the photoelectric effect we need to use the **photon model** of light. In this model we regard light as packets or **quanta** (singular: **quantum**) of energy. The energy of a quantum or photon of light depends on the frequency of the radiation.

According to Max Planck, the energy E of the quantum of radiation (photon) of frequency f is given by:

$E = hf$ where E = energy of the photon in J
h = Planck's constant 6.63×10^{-34} J s
f = frequency of the radiation in Hz

$E = \frac{hc}{\lambda}$

Einstein assumed that not only were light and other forms of electromagnetic radiation emitted in whole numbers of photons, but that they were also absorbed as photons. But first, we need to define what physicists call the work function of a metal.

The **work function** Φ is defined as the minimum quantity of energy needed to liberate electrons from the surface of a metal and to just allow it to escape to an infinite distance from the metal. Einstein proposed that a photon of energy will cause the emission of an electron from the metal if the energy of the photon is equal to or greater than the work function of the metal.

If the photon's energy is greater than the work function of the metal then the difference appears as kinetic energy of the ejected electron. Since the work function is the **minimum** energy needed to eject an electron from the metal this means that the electrons that are ejected have a range of kinetic energy from zero to a maximum. Hence we can write:

$$\tfrac{1}{2}mv^2_{max} = hf - \Phi$$

This is known as **Einstein's Photoelectric Equation.**

The frequency of electromagnetic radiation that just liberates electrons from a

Does not depend on intensity, rather colour (frequency.)

metal is known as the **threshold frequency** f_o. The photons of this frequency have energy equal to the work function of the metal. Hence:

$\Phi = hf_o$

Combining the two equations above therefore gives

$\frac{1}{2} mv^2_{max} = hf - hf_o$

On formula sheet [handwritten]

The electron-volt (eV)

The kinetic energy of a photo electron, the work function and the energy of a photon can all be measured in joules (J). However the electron-volt (eV) is often used as an alternative unit for energy when dealing with these quantities.

The work function is measured in joules or electron-volts. An electron-volt (eV) is defined as the energy an electron gains or loses when it moves through a potential difference of 1 volt.

$1 \text{ eV} = 1.6 \times 10^{-19} \text{ J}$

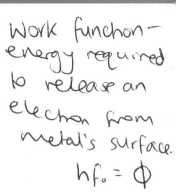

Work function — energy required to release an electron from metal's surface. $hf_o = \Phi$ [handwritten]

Worked example

1 A strip of magnesium ribbon in an evacuated chamber is illuminated with monochromatic light of wavelength 300 nm. The work function of magnesium is 2.8 eV. Calculate the following:

(a) the photoelectric threshold frequency for magnesium.

(b) the frequency and energy of a photon in the incident beam.

(c) in what part of the electromagnetic spectrum radiation of wavelength 300 nm is found.

Solution

(a) $\Phi = 2.8 \text{ eV} = 2.8 \times 1.6 \times 10^{-19} \text{ J} = 4.48 \times 10^{-19} \text{ J}$

$f_o = \Phi \div h = (4.48 \times 10^{-19}) \div 6.63 \times 10^{-34} = 6.76 \times 10^{14} \text{ Hz}$

(b) $f = c \div \lambda = 3 \times 10^8 \div 300 \times 10^{-9} = 1 \times 10^{15} \text{ Hz}$

$E = hf = 6.63 \times 10^{-34} \times 1 \times 10^{15} = 6.63 \times 10^{-19} \text{ J}$

(c) Radiation of wavelength 300 nm is found in the ultraviolet region of the spectrum.

Exercise 2.5A

1 (a) The work function of a certain metal is 2.7 eV.

(i) Write 2.7 eV in joules, giving your answer in standard form.

(ii) What is meant by the statement *"The work function of a certain metal is 2.7 eV"*?

(iii) Does photoelectric emission occur when light of wavelength 450 nm falls incident on the surface of this metal? Justify your answer with an appropriate calculation.

(b) Another metal, with a work function of 3.7×10^{-19} J, is illuminated with light of frequency 630 THz. The surface then emits photoelectrons, causing the metal to acquire a positive potential and stop emitting further photoelectrons.

   (i) Write 630 THz in hertz, giving your answer in standard form.

   (ii) Calculate the maximum kinetic energy of the photoelectrons emitted, giving your answer in eV.

   (iii) Use your answer to write down the electric potential of the metal surface, in volts, which just prevents further photoelectric emission. (No further mathematics required.)

2 A monochromatic light source emits 50 J of light energy per second, with each photon in the beam having a wavelength of 450 nm. Only half of the light energy emitted by the source falls incident on a freshly cut potassium surface. Potassium emits photoelectrons only when the incident light has a wavelength of 550 nm or less.

   Only one in every million of the incident photons liberates a photoelectron from the surface.

   (a) What do physicists mean by 'a photon of light'?

   (b) (i) Calculate the energy of a single light photon emitted by this source.

   (ii) How many such photons are emitted by the source every second?

   (iii) How many photons strike the potassium surface every second?

   (iv) How many photoelectrons are emitted by the potassium every second?

   (v) How much electrical charge is liberated by the potassium surface every second?

   (vi) Use the definition of current to write down the size of the electric current that can be drawn from the potassium surface using this arrangement. (No further mathematics required.)

   (c) The source is now replaced with another which emits 100 J of light energy per second, with each photon in the beam having a wavelength of 600 nm. All other aspects of the arrangements are unchanged. How many electrons would now be liberated from the surface of the potassium in 1 second?

3 The table below shows the results of a photoelectric emission experiment.

Max KE of photoelectrons, E / 10^{-20} J	15.0	10.0	6.00	4.29	2.73
Wavelength of light used, λ / nm	400	450	500	525	550

Given that $E = hc(\dfrac{1}{\lambda} - \dfrac{1}{\lambda_0})$, use the data to draw a suitable straight line graph from which the Planck constant (h) and the cut-off wavelength (λ_0) might be found. You will need to copy the table above and complete it. Be sure to label the table headings and the graph axes correctly. The third row has been left blank for your use.

The evidence for energy levels in atoms

When sunlight is made to pass through a triangular glass prism, a spectrum is obtained. We observe a range of colours which gradually changes from deep red through orange to yellow and so on to violet. There are no sudden changes of colour and no gaps. Between the limits of red light and violet light all possible colours, and hence all possible wavelengths, are present. We call such a spectrum **continuous**. We can also obtain a continuous spectrum from hot filament lamps.

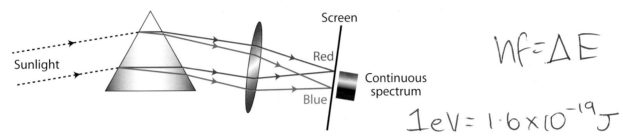

$$hf = \Delta E$$

$$1 eV = 1.6 \times 10^{-19} J$$

However, when we look at the light from a gas discharge lamp containing a gaseous element, such as sodium vapour or neon, we obtain a very limited range of wavelengths indeed, for example:

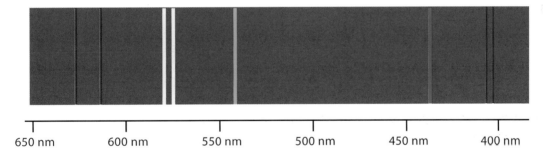

Why do elements like sodium give an emission spectrum consisting of a series of discrete wavelengths? In the early years of the twentieth century, physicists simply had no answer as to why this should be so.

Niels Bohr, a Danish physicist and friend of Albert Einstein, made a remarkable suggestion to explain atomic line spectra. Bohr's idea was that electrons in atoms could orbit the nucleus only in certain allowed circular paths.

An electron has a fixed amount of energy in each orbit, those being closest to the nucleus having the least energy and those most distant from the nucleus having the most energy. Each orbit therefore has an energy level associated with it. Electrons orbiting a nucleus are in bound states and must acquire a minimum quantity of energy to break free from the attraction of the nucleus.

An electron at an infinite separation from the nucleus is considered to have zero energy. The energy of the electrons in the bound states is therefore considered to be negative. When an electron in an atom has the lowest possible energy, then that electron is said to be in its ground state.

Bohr argued that an electron could move from one energy level to a higher energy level by absorbing a photon of energy equal to the energy difference between the two states. This process is called **excitation**. As a result, the electron moves to an unstable, higher energy state and the exciting photon ceases to exist.

149

Similarly, if an electron in an excited state moves from a high energy level to a vacant lower energy level, a photon of light of energy exactly equal to the energy difference between the two states will be emitted. This process is called **relaxation**.

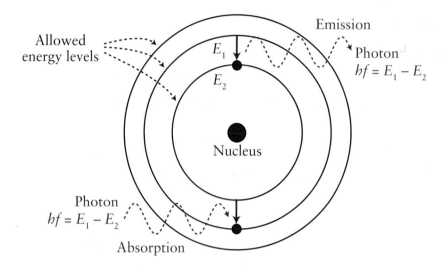

For both excitation and relaxation the same equation is true:

$hf = \Delta E$ where ΔE = energy difference between the two levels (J)

h = Planck's constant = 6.63×10^{-34} J s

f = the frequency of the photon emitted or absorbed (Hz)

You should appreciate that the equation above is an example of the principle of conservation of energy in a form that applies to electron transitions between orbits.

The diagram below is called an **energy level diagram** and it shows the main electron transitions in hydrogen. The lowest energy level or ground state has a value of –13.6 eV. Higher energy levels are less negative, –3.4 eV, –1.5 eV and so on. The difference between the energy levels gradually becomes smaller as the energy of each level increases. There is an infinite number of energy levels.

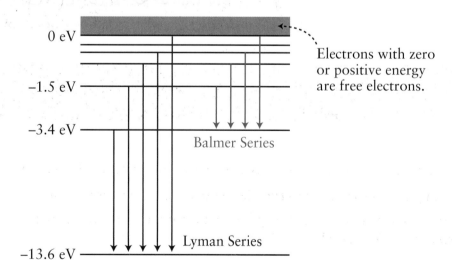

Lyman series

The longest wavelength in this series corresponds to a photon with minimum energy. This photon is emitted when the electron moves from level with energy –3.4 eV to the ground state level with energy –13.6 eV.

The energy of the emitted photon = 13.6 – 3.4 = 10.2 eV = 1.63×10^{-18} J = hf or $\dfrac{hc}{\lambda}$.

This gives a frequency of 2.46×10^{15} Hz and a wavelength of 121.9 nm.

The shortest wavelength in this series corresponds to a photon with maximum energy.

This photon is emitted when the electron moves from an energy of 0 to the ground state level of energy –13.6 eV.

The energy of the emitted photon = 13.6 – 0 = 13.6 eV = 2.18×10^{-18} J = hf or $\dfrac{hc}{\lambda}$.

This gives a frequency of 3.29×10^{15} Hz and a wavelength of 91.2 nm.

Balmer series

Performing an analysis similar to that used for the Lyman series gives the following:

The longest wavelength photon has an energy of 1.9 eV, frequency = 4.59×10^{14} Hz and wavelength = 654 nm (red).

The shortest wavelength photon has an energy of 3.4 eV, frequency = 8.21×10^{14} Hz and wavelength = 365 nm (UV).

Exercise 2.5B

1 Below is a picture of a continuous spectrum and an emission spectrum.

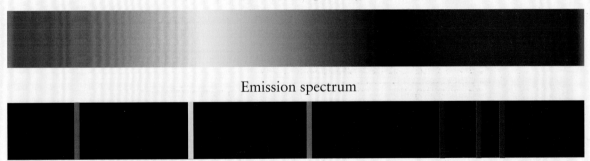

Continuous spectrum

Emission spectrum

(a) How might a continuous spectrum be produced and observed in a school laboratory?

(b) (i) How might a hydrogen emission spectrum be observed in a school laboratory?

(ii) Describe what is happening within the hydrogen atom when one of the lines in the emission spectrum is produced.

(iii) The red line in the emission spectrum of hydrogen has a wavelength of 655 nm. Use the energy level diagram below to identify the transition which brings about this emission. Copy the diagram and indicate with an arrow the direction of the transition.

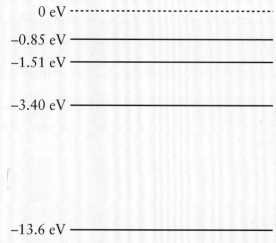

$$0 \text{ eV} \cdots\cdots\cdots\cdots\cdots\cdots\cdots\cdots\cdots$$

$$-0.85 \text{ eV} \underline{\hspace{5cm}}$$
$$-1.51 \text{ eV} \underline{\hspace{5cm}}$$

$$-3.40 \text{ eV} \underline{\hspace{5cm}}$$

$$-13.6 \text{ eV} \underline{\hspace{5cm}}$$

2 (a) What do physicists mean by the 'ground state' when referring to the energy level diagram for hydrogen?

Refer to the energy level diagram above for parts (b) and (c).

(b) How much more energy is required to completely remove an electron in the ground state than an electron in the first excited state?

(c) Show that any electron transition in the hydrogen atom which terminates in the ground state gives rise to a photon in the ultraviolet region of the spectrum.

3 In the spectrum of atomic hydrogen the wavelength, λ, corresponding to transitions from high energy levels ($n \geq 2$) and the ground state ($n = 1$), is given by the Rydberg formula:

$$\frac{1}{\lambda} = R\left(1 - \frac{1}{n^2}\right)$$

where R is a constant known as the Rydberg constant.

Wavelengths for this series of spectral lines are shown in the table below.

n	2	3	4	5	6
$1/n^2$					
λ / nm	122	103	97	95	94
$1/\lambda$ / nm^{-1}					

(a) Copy and complete the table above.

(b) Plot the graph of $\frac{1}{\lambda}$ (vertical axis) against $\frac{1}{n^2}$ (horizontal axis).

(Hint: Do not start from zero on the vertical axis.)

(c) Use the graph to show that the value of the Rydberg constant is approximately 1.1×10^7 m^{-1}.

Laser action

Lasers were first invented in the late 1950s and today we see lasers being used almost everywhere. They are used in optical fibre broadband connections, in telephony, in barcode scanners and to measure the distances between celestial bodies in space. For example, the distance between the Moon and Earth can be measured to within 15 cm using laser technology. They are also used by surgeons to arrest bleeding, by metal workers to cut through metal, by tradespeople to obtain a 'level' during construction, and by teachers and lecturers in optical pointers.

The photons emitted by a laser are coherent, they have the same wavelength and they are in exactly the same phase (or more accurately, they maintain exactly the same phase difference all the time).

In nature, there are normally many more electrons in the ground state than in any excited state. The length of time an electron spends in an excited state is typically 10^{-8}s. It then makes a transition to a lower energy level and a photon of light is emitted. This is a random process and is called **spontaneous emission**.

In a laser, we need to have more electrons in the excited state than in the ground state. This is called a **population inversion**. Electrons can exist in some states for a much greater time than in normal states. These are called **metastable states** and the time spent can be around 10^{-3}s. This is 100 000 times longer than normal. This gives us time to have more electrons in this excited state than in the ground state.

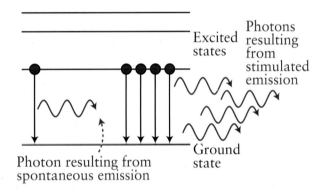

However electrons in a metastable excited state can be induced to make a transition by the presence of a photon of energy equal to the difference between the levels. This is known as **stimulated emission**. This 'inducing' photon results from spontaneous emission. Stimulated emission is extremely unlikely to occur in nature.

Note that the photons produced by stimulated emission are not only coherent, but they are exactly in phase with one another. So the wave produced is greatly amplified, hence the acronym 'laser' (light amplification by stimulated emission of radiation).

The helium-neon laser is commonly found in schools but can still be dangerous. Looking into the laser beam must be avoided. It is just as dangerous to look at a 1mW He-Ne laser as it is to look directly at the Sun on a clear day.

A diagrammatic view of laser action

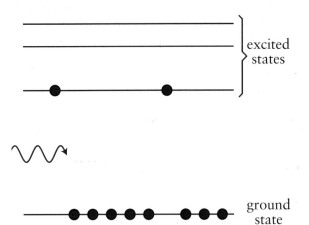

Stimulated emission is very unlikely because there are many more electrons in the ground state than in the excited state. Excitation is therefore more probable than stimulated emission.

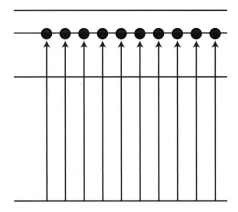

The first stage in achieving a population inversion is to cause the majority of the electrons in the ground state to move to an excited state by optical pumping. But the excited state is short lived.

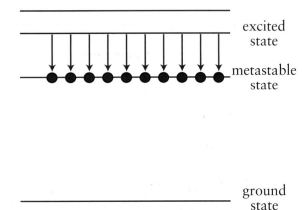

Electrons in the excited, short lived state quickly relax to the metastable state, where they can remain for much longer than in an ordinary excited state.

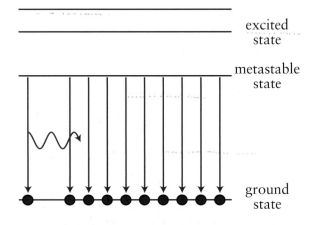

The photon generated by the first (and spontaneous) relaxation from the metastable state causes the other electrons in the metastable state to return to the ground state by stimulated emission.

X-rays

How are X-rays Produced?

Note: the specification only requires students to have a knowledge of the production of X-rays by the process of electron movement between energy levels. This is described in '3 The characteristic line emission spectrum' (page 156).

X-rays are produced by high speed electrons striking metal targets in an evacuated tube. The electrons are emitted by a **cathode** which is heated to a very high temperature (white heat). This heating is produced by an electric current passing through the cathode. The electrons are then accelerated toward a metal **anode** using a very high voltage (typically 100 kV).

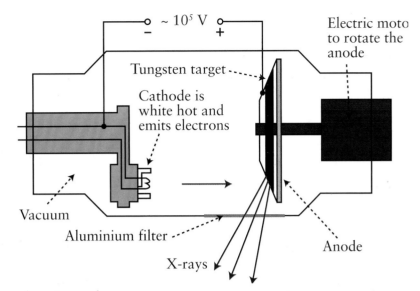

At the centre of the anode is a metal target. This target is made of metal of a high melting point and high atomic number. Around **0.5%** of the electrons produce **X-rays**, the other 99.5% simply heat the anode. The anode therefore needs to be constantly cooled. In the case of the rotating anode tube shown in the top right diagram, this is achieved by conduction, convection and radiation.

The graph on the right shows a typical X-ray spectrum. There are three characteristics that must be understood:

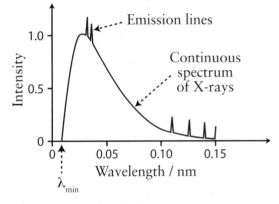

1 The continuous spectrum

When the high speed electrons encounter the atoms of the target material they are slowed. The energy lost by the electron appears as an X-ray photon. The electrons lose varying amounts of energy so X-ray photons of different energy (wavelength, frequency) are produced. This type of X-ray production is known as **braking radiation,** as shown in the bottom right diagram.

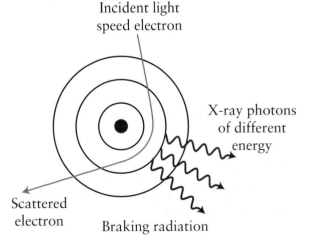

2 The minimum wavelength λ_{min}

Some high speed electrons lose all of their kinetic energy in a single encounter with the atoms of the target material. This produces an X-ray photon with maximum energy (minimum wavelength or maximum frequency). The value of λ_{min} can be calculated.

The kinetic energy of the electron = loss of electric potential energy = eV
where e is the charge of the electron
         V is the tube voltage

The energy of this X-ray photon = $\dfrac{hc}{\lambda_{min}} = eV.$

155

3   The characteristic line emission spectrum

These are characteristic of the element used as the target. These elements have high atomic numbers and consequently the electron shells are generally filled with the total complement of electrons. An incoming electron will knock an electron out of these filled electron shells, as shown in the diagram on the right. The vacancy left is immediately filled by an electron from a higher energy shell dropping down to a lower energy shell. It loses its energy as an X-ray of very specific energy or wavelength.

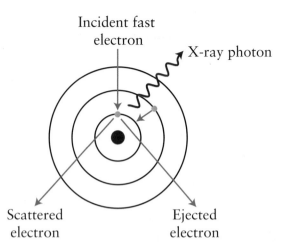

Incident fast electron

X-ray photon

Scattered electron

Ejected electron

The metal target

In all atoms of low atomic number transitions to the innermost shell give rise to the emission of ultraviolet light. It is for this reason that metals like aluminium are quite unsuitable as targets in an X-ray tube. Their sharp emission lines (emission spectra) have wavelengths higher than X-rays.

Low atomic number elements also have insufficient extra-nuclear electrons to slow an incoming electron quickly enough to give braking radiation (also called Bremsstrahlung, from the German for braking radiation) in the X-ray region. The radiation emitted again is of higher wavelength.

Computed tomography or CT scanning

Computed tomography (CT) imaging, also known as 'CAT scanning' (computed axial tomography), was developed in the early to mid 1970s. CT has the unique ability to image a combination of soft tissue, bone and blood vessels. Today CT enables the diagnosis of a wide range of illness and combines the use of a digital computer with a rotating X-ray device to create detailed cross-sectional images or 'slices' of the different organs and body parts, such as the lungs, liver, kidneys, brain, spine and blood vessels.

A conventional X-ray image of the head (middle right) can show only the dense bone structures of the skull. CT images (bottom right) allow us to see soft-tissue structures like the valves of the heart or grey and white matter in the brain.

CT is an invaluable tool in the cancer diagnosis process and is often the preferred method for diagnosing lung, liver and pancreatic cancer.

CT imaging has a role in the detection, diagnosis and treatment of heart disease, acute stroke and vascular diseases which can lead to stroke. Additionally, CT can be used to measure bone mineral density for the detection of osteoporosis.

A conventional X-ray image

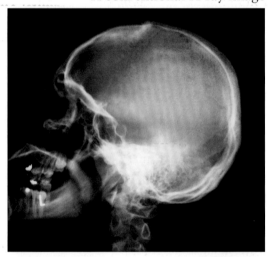

CT images

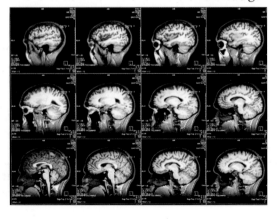

CT has excellent application in trauma cases and other emergencies. All dedicated trauma departments have a CT scanner so patients can be scanned immediately to look for major internal injuries, such as internal bleeding.

CT is used extensively for diagnosing problems of the inner ears and sinuses because of its ability to generate very high resolution images. The anatomy of the inner ear and sinuses is made up of delicate soft tissue structures and very fine bones. CT is excellent for imaging tumours or polyps in the sinuses and diseases that cause degeneration of the small bones in the inner ear.

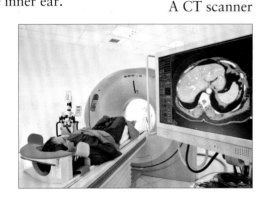

A CT scanner

Unlike other medical imaging techniques, such as conventional X-ray imaging (radiography), CT enables direct imaging and shows the differences within soft tissue structures, such as liver, lung tissue and fat. CT imaging of the head and brain can detect tumours, show blood clots and blood vessel defects. Due to the short scan times (500 milliseconds to a few seconds), CT can be used for all regions of the body, including where the body is in motion, such as breathing.

How is CT scanning carried out?

During the scan the patient lies on a bed, with the body part under examination placed in the round tunnel or opening of the scanner. The bed then moves slowly backwards and forwards to allow the scanner to take pictures of the body, although it does not touch the patient. The length of the test depends on the number of pictures and the different angles taken.

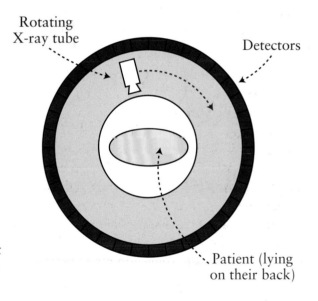

The X-ray tube is rotated around the patient. There is a large number of detectors on a complete circle around the patient. This means that a complete scan can be completed in less than 5 seconds. This is much safer for the patient and it is less likely that the image will be affected by the patient moving. The computer is able to reconstruct the structures within the body from the detector signal using sophisticated software.

Disadvantages of CT scanning

Computed tomography is considerably more expensive than conventional radiography. As a rough guide, a chest X-ray might cost £10–£25 whereas a computed tomogram of the chest could cost £50 to £150.

Secondly, the X-ray dose from CT is much larger than for conventional radiography. During CT of the chest the patient receives the equivalent dose to that from 100 chest radiographs.

Another factor to consider is patient preparation. For scans of the abdomen patients often have to drink several large cupfuls of contrast agent about an hour before scanning. The contrast agent has a high density so in the scan the entire bowel is highlighted in white and readily distinguished from possible intra-abdominal masses. Because of the large X-ray dose from CT other methods are always considered before CT is carried out on children, as they are particularly sensitive to radiation.

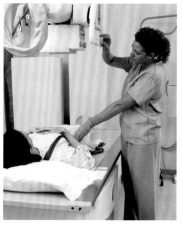

A modern medical X-ray machine

Conventional X-rays

Within the human body denser objects, such as bones, absorb more radiation than less dense material, such as muscle. Traditionally the detector used was very sensitive photographic film, but modern hospitals now use digital detectors, which are faster, cheaper, use less non-renewable materials and produce no waste.

In general, the subject to be X-rayed is placed between the X-ray source and the detector. The radiographers withdraw to a place of safety behind a lead screen and the X-rays are generated. This is why bones appear white on X-ray images. The bones absorb more X-rays and their 'shadow' is cast on the X-ray film. Specially trained doctors called radiologists can read these images to diagnose medical conditions or injuries.

A conventional (or regular) medical X-ray produces a two-dimensional picture that can help find fractures (broken bones), tumours and foreign objects.

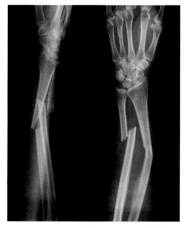

A conventional medical X-ray

Exercise 2.5C

1 (a) Draw a large labelled diagram to show the main parts of a modern X-ray tube.

   (b) Most of the kinetic energy of the electrons striking the target in an X-ray is converted into heat. Discuss briefly two ways by which this heat is removed from the target.

   (c) Account briefly for the continuous part of the X-ray spectrum.

   (d) X-ray spectra typically show discrete lines at particular wavelengths. Give a brief account of the source of these discrete lines.

   (e) A particular X-ray tube uses a tungsten target and the tube voltage is 100 kV.

   (i) Use the Principle of Conservation of Energy to show that the minimum wavelength of the X-rays from this tube is 1.24×10^{-11} m.

   (ii) What change in the X-ray spectrum would be observed if copper was used instead of tungsten as the target?

2 (a) A patient is to undergo a CT scan. Describe what happens.

   (b) Give three reasons why a doctor might decide against giving a patient a CT scan.

2.6 Wave-Particle Duality

You should be able to:

2.6.1 Categorise electromagnetic wave phenomena as being explained by the wave model, the photon model or both

2.6.2 Describe electron diffraction

2.6.3 Use the de Broglie equation $\lambda = \dfrac{h}{p}$

One of the amazing success stories of nineteenth century physics was the development of the wave theory of light. It was used to deepen our understanding of the transmission of light, of reflection and refraction, of dispersion and, most spectacularly, of interference and diffraction. Moreover, the realisation that light could be polarised seemed to prove beyond doubt that light was not only a wave, but that it was a transverse wave.

It came as a shock when Einstein demonstrated conclusively that an explanation of the photoelectric effect required us to consider light as a stream of particles or photons. Einstein explained the observations associated with the photoelectric effect using the idea that light and other forms of electromagnetic radiation were both emitted in whole numbers of quanta and absorbed as quanta. A quantum is a discrete amount of energy. The energy of a quantum (photon) of electromagnetic radiation is given by $E = hf$ or $E = \dfrac{hc}{\lambda}$

This implied that electromagnetic radiation could exhibit particle-like behaviour when being emitted or absorbed and led to the idea that light has a dual nature. In some circumstances it appears to behave as waves (reflection, refraction, diffraction, interference and polarisation) and in others as particles (photoelectric effect and line emission).

Therefore to explain some aspects of light behavior, such as interference and diffraction, it is treated as a wave. To explain other aspects it is treated as being made up of particles. Light exhibits wave-particle duality, because it exhibits properties of both waves and particles.

Phenomenon	Can be explained in terms of waves	Can be explained in terms of photons
Interference of light	Yes	No
Diffraction of light	Yes	No
Polarisation of light	Yes	No
Photoelectric effect	No	Yes

Some phenomena, like reflection and refraction, can be explained in terms of both the wave theory and the particle theory of light.

$n\lambda = d \sin \theta$

Electron diffraction

The wave-particle nature of light caused some physicists to consider if matter (beams of particles) could exhibit wave-like properties. In 1924, Louis de Broglie (pronounced de Broy), having considered the particle-wave duality of light, presented a thesis suggesting that matter might also have a dual nature. The proposal was that a particle, having a momentum p, has an associated wavelength λ, given by:

$$\lambda = \frac{h}{p}$$

where λ = de Broglie wavelength (m)
h = Planck's constant (6.63×10^{-34} J s)
p = momentum of the particle (kg m s^{-1})

De Broglie's suggestion that electrons with momentum possessed an associated wavelength was followed up by two enterprising physicists called Davisson and Germer. In 1926 they succeeded in obtaining a circular diffraction pattern using electrons and a nickel crystal.

Calculations show that if electrons were accelerated through 100 V then their momentum would indicate a wavelength of around 10^{-10} m. This is the distance between atoms and so it might be possible to use the layers of atoms in a crystal to produce diffraction and interference effects.

This can be demonstrated using the apparatus below. It shows how a crystal of graphite can be used to produce interference of electrons in a beam. Where lots of electrons reach the fluorescent screen a bright ring is seen. This is a region of constructive interference. The absence of light from the screen indicates a region of destructive interference: few electrons reach the screen.

red diffracted most

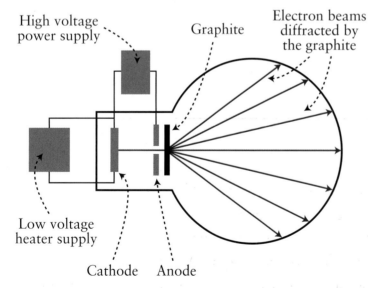

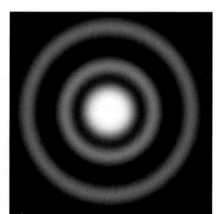

Electron diffraction rings
seen on the fluorescent screen

It appears that wave-particle duality is not confined to light. Everything exhibits wave-particle duality, from electrons to golf balls. The behaviour of relatively large objects, such as a golf ball, is dominated by their particle nature, but to explain the behaviour of very small things, such as electrons, both the wave properties and particle properties have to be considered. The experiment discussed on page 160 shows that electrons exhibit the same kind of interference pattern as light does when it passes through a double slit (Young's experiment).

If the accelerating voltage is increased, the speed of the diffracting electrons (and hence their momentum) also increases. The rings then become narrower and have a smaller radius, showing that the wavelengths of the electron waves decrease with increasing momentum.

Why then do we not observe other moving objects, such as cars, trains and buses, displaying wave-like properties? The answer is that their mass (and hence their momentum) is so large and Planck's constant is so small, that the wavelength of these objects is much too small to produce observable interference and diffraction effects.

Exercise 2.6

1   Some phenomena can only be explained using a particle theory, other phenomena can only be explained using a wave theory. A few phenomena can be explained using either a particle or a wave theory.

(a) In the table below indicate with a letter 'P' if the phenomenon can only be explained using a particle theory, a 'W' if it can only be explained using a wave theory and an 'E if it can be explained with either a particle or a wave theory.

Phenomenon	Theory used to explain the phenomenon
Diffraction of an electron beam	
Diffraction of light	
Interference of light	
Polarisation	
Photoelectric effect	
Reflection of light	
Refraction of light	

(b) Describe the experiment to show how a beam of electrons can be diffracted.

2   (a) A certain electron in a hydrogen atom has a kinetic energy of 2.2×10^{-18} J.

(i) Show that this electron has a speed of 2.2×10^6 m s^{-1}.

(ii) Calculate the magnitude of the momentum of this electron.

(iii) Use de Broglie's equation to find the wavelength of this electron.

(b) Explain why a bullet of mass 25 g travelling at 400 m s^{-1} through the air is unlikely to produce observable diffraction effects.

3   A particle moving at 2×10^6 m s^{-1} has a de Broglie wavelength of 3.64×10^{-10} m. Find the probable identity of the particle.

2.7 Astronomy

You should be able to:

2.7.1   Recall, demonstrate an understanding of and apply the classical equations for Doppler shift to find the wavelength of the waves received by a stationary observer from a moving source

2.7.2   Demonstrate an understanding of the difference between cosmological red shift and Doppler red shift

2.7.3   Calculate the cosmological red shift parameter, z, of a receding galaxy using
$z = \dfrac{\Delta\lambda}{\lambda}$ and use $z = \dfrac{v}{c}$ to find the recession speed v, where $v \ll c$

2.7.4   Use Hubble's Law $v = H_o d$ to estimate the distance, d, to a distant galaxy, given the value of its speed of recession, v, and the Hubble constant, $H_o \approx 2.4 \times 10^{-18}\ \text{s}^{-1}$

2.7.5   Recall and use $T = \dfrac{1}{H_o}$ to estimate the age of the universe

$c = f\lambda$

Red shift – the Doppler Effect

If a wave source is moving, the crests of its waves get bunched together in front of the wave source. If the wave crests are bunched together, their wavelength decreases. On the other side of the source, the waves spread out and the wavelength increases. This is known as the Doppler Effect. The Doppler Effect explains why the sound of a siren from a fire engine appears to have a bigger pitch (smaller wavelength) as it approaches us and a smaller pitch (bigger wavelength) as it moves away from us.

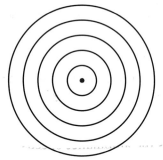
Wavefronts for a stationary source

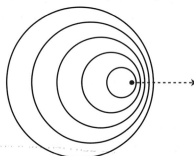
Wavefronts for a source moving to the right. (Red shift to the left of the source, blue shift to the right.)

Doppler shift is used by some traffic police to find the speed of passing motorists. The machine transmits a microwave signal of known frequency, f_o. The frequency of the echo received from the target vehicle, f_r, is then compared with f_o. The greater the difference between f_r and f_o, the greater the speed of the target vehicle.

In the case of light we use the terms 'blue shift' and 'red shift' to describe how movement of the source changes the wavelength. Being blue-shifted or red-shifted does not mean that the light becomes blue or red. It means simply that the **light's wavelength either is shortened (blue-shifted) because the object giving off the light is approaching, or is lengthened (red-shifted) because the object is moving away from the observer.**

The Doppler Effect with sound

In classical physics, where the speeds of source and the receiver relative to the medium are lower than the velocity of waves in the medium, the relationship between observed frequency f and emitted frequency f_o is given by:

$$f = \left(\frac{v_w + v_r}{v_w + v_s}\right) f_o$$

where v_w is the velocity of waves in the medium.

         v_r is the velocity of the receiver relative to the medium; positive if the receiver is moving towards the source (and negative in the other direction).

         v_s is the velocity of the source relative to the medium; positive if the source is moving away from the receiver (and negative in the other direction).

At AS level, we are only interested in situations where the observer is stationary, so $v_r = 0$ and the equation reduces to:

$$f = \left(\frac{v_w}{v_w + v_s}\right) f_o$$

LLAP

Taking the reciprocal of both sides and then multiplying by v_w gives:

$$\lambda = \left(1 + \frac{v_s}{v_w}\right) \lambda_o$$

> **Note:** the last two equations should be memorised.

Worked example

1 The siren mounted on an ambulance emits sound of wavelength 0.46 m. A stationary observer detects a sound of wavelength 0.42 m as the ambulance comes towards him. The speed of sound is 340 m s^{-1}. Assume the ambulance is travelling at a constant speed.

(a) Calculate the speed of the ambulance.

(b) Calculate the wavelength detected by a stationary observer as the ambulance speeds away from him.

Solution

(a) The velocity of the source is now considered negative since it is moving towards the observer.

$$\lambda = \left(1 + \frac{v_s}{v_w}\right) \lambda_o \quad \text{so} \quad 0.42 = \left(1 - \frac{v_s}{340}\right) \times 0.46$$

Rearranging gives: $v_s = \left(1 - \frac{0.42}{0.46}\right) \times 340 = 29.57 \text{ m s}^{-1}$

(b) The velocity of the source is now considered positive since it is moving away from the observer.

$$\lambda = \left(1 + \frac{v_s}{v_w}\right) \lambda_o = \left(1 + \frac{29.57}{340}\right) \times 0.46 = 0.50 \text{ m}$$

Doppler Effect in astronomy

On Earth physicists analysing light from hydrogen gas in a laboratory get intense peaks at wavelengths of 410.2 nm, 434.0 nm, 486.1 nm, and 656.3 nm. This is called the emission spectrum of hydrogen.

In the 1920s, Edwin Hubble, while studying the stars of distant galaxies, found that for some, their emission spectrum had peaks at 411.54 nm, 435.50 nm, 487.75 nm and 658.47 nm.

Hubble knew that these wavelengths did not correspond to any known element. He also noticed that these spectral lines corresponded to hydrogen's emission spectrum, except that they were all about 0.3% longer in wavelength than they should have been for hydrogen.

Wavelength of light in nm from hydrogen in laboratory	Wavelength of light in nm from hydrogen in a distant star
410.2	411.5
434.0	435.5
486.1	487.8
656.3	658.6

Hubble concluded that this red shift must be because the stars in these galaxies were moving away from earth at about 1×10^6 m s^{-1} (one million metres per second!). Red shift is accepted by all physicists as convincing evidence that the universe is continuously expanding.

Cosmological Doppler Effect

So far we have thought about the Doppler Effect in terms of the movement of the source towards or away from the observer. Cosmologists have a different perspective. They ask this question – how is the light we observe from different galaxies affected by the fact that the universe itself is expanding?

Cosmologists think of the expanding universe as the expansion of **space itself**. So light waves from a distant galaxy are being stretched as the space between us and that galaxy increases. This is called **cosmological red shift** to distinguish it from red shift produced by sources that are moving through space.

The mathematics of ordinary and cosmological red shift are the same – we just need to know what the equations are and how to use them.

Physicists define a quantity called the z-parameter (or red shift parameter), by the equations:

$$z = \frac{\Delta\lambda}{\lambda} = \frac{\Delta f}{f} = \frac{v}{c}$$

Note: you should memorise this equation.

where λ is the emitted wavelength

          f is the emitted frequency

          $\Delta\lambda$ is the difference between the observed and the emitted wavelengths

Δf is the difference between the observed and the emitted frequencies

v is the velocity of the source in the observer's direction

c is the speed of the waves in the medium

In the case of light, the equation is only valid if $v << c$. As v approaches c, the equation changes due to relativistic effects.

Confusingly, the z-parameter itself is sometimes called the red shift in some textbooks and on the Internet.

Don't get worried about plus and minus signs in these equations. Clearly if there is an increase in wavelength (red shift), Δλ is positive. But if Δλ is positive, there will be a reduction in frequency, so Δf is negative. Just ignore that. We are only interested is the size of the change, not its sign. But we need to know that:

- the wavelength increases (and the frequency decreases) if the source is moving away from the observer.
- the wavelength decreases (and the frequency increases) if the source is moving towards the observer.

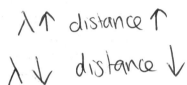

λ↑ distance ↑
λ↓ distance ↓

Worked examples

Let's first re-visit the previous Worked Example on the sound from a passing ambulance.

1 The siren mounted on an ambulance emits sound of wavelength 0.46 m. A stationary observer detects a sound of wavelength 0.42 m as the ambulance comes towards him. The speed of sound is 340 m s^{-1}. Assume the ambulance is travelling at a constant speed.

(a) Calculate the speed of the ambulance.

(b) Calculate the wavelength detected by a stationary observer as the ambulance speeds away from him.

Solution

(a) The velocity of the source is now considered negative since it is moving towards the observer.

$$z = \frac{\Delta\lambda}{\lambda} = \frac{\Delta f}{f} = \frac{v}{c}$$

$$\Delta\lambda = \lambda \times \frac{v_{ambulance}}{v_{sound}}$$

$$v_{ambulance} = \frac{0.04 \times 340}{0.46} = 29.57 \text{ m s}^{-1}$$

(b) Δλ = 0.04 m, so the observed wavelength = 0.04 + 0.46 = 0.50 m

Note: we added the value of Δλ because the ambulance was moving away from the observer.

2 There is an absorption line in the spectrum of calcium which has a wavelength 393.3 nm. The same line in the spectrum of the light from a distant galaxy has a wavelength of 394.1 nm.

(a) Calcuate the z-parameter for this galaxy.

(b) Calculate the speed with which this galaxy is moving with respect to the Earth.

(c) In what direction is the galaxy moving relative to the Earth?

Solution

(a) $z = \dfrac{\Delta\lambda}{\lambda} = \dfrac{394.1 - 393.3}{393.3} = \dfrac{0.8}{393.3} \cong 0.002$

(note that z has no unit)

(b) $v = zc = 0.002 \times 3\times10^8 = 6\times10^5$ m s^{-1}

(c) Since there is an increase in the observed wavelength (red shift), the galaxy is moving away from the Earth.

We say the galaxy is *receding* with a *recession* speed of 6×10^5 m s^{-1}.

Receding simply means it is moving *away* from us.

Hubble's Law

In the early part of the twentieth century astronomers concluded that apart from a few very close ones, all galaxies showed a red shift. This meant that they were moving away from us. A graph of recessional velocity, v against distance, d was a straight line through the origin indicating direct proportion. It was proof that the universe was expanding.

This graph gives rise to Hubble's Law, named in honour of Edwin Hubble who did much to confirm the relationship. Expressed as an equation, Hubble's Law is written:

$$v = H_o d$$

where v is the recessional velocity

         d is the distance between Earth and the galaxy in question

         H_o is the Hubble parameter (also called the Hubble constant)

Many physicists prefer to call it the Hubble parameter, rather than the Hubble constant, as there is evidence to believe that the rate at which the universe is expanding, and hence **the value of H, has changed over time**. For that reason, it is written with a subscript zero, to denote explicitly that we are using the current value of H. In SI units the approximate value of H_o is 2.4×10^{-18} s^{-1}.

Note: the specification uses the term Hubble constant.

Worked example

The Sombrero Galaxy has a z parameter (red shift) of 0.003416.
Calculate its speed of recession and its distance from our galaxy.

Solution

Recessional speed, $v = zc$
$$= 0.003416 \times 3 \times 10^8 = 1.02 \times 10^6 \text{ m s}^{-1}$$

$$d = \frac{v}{H_o} = \frac{1.02 \times 10^6}{2.4 \times 10^{-18}} = 4.25 \times 10^{23} \text{ m}$$

The Sombrero Galaxy
NASA/ESA and The Hubble Heritage Team STScI/AURA

The age of the universe

Hubble realised that the light from distant galaxies is red-shifted and that the more distant they are, the greater the red shift. Today, this is interpreted to mean that the universe is expanding: that is, the distance between galaxies is increasing. This is in much the same way as marks on the surface of a balloon get further apart when the balloon in inflated.

Hubble's interpretation was slightly different: he took the results to mean that galaxies were receding from each other through space. Now, if you imagine time in the Universe running backwards, how long would it take a distant galaxy to reach you? Answering this question tells you how long ago it is since all the galaxies were together in the same place, i.e. how long ago the Big Bang occurred. (The Big Bang is the moment when physicists believe that the entire universe was compressed to a single point.) By rearranging Hubble's equation, the time taken for a galaxy travelling at speed v to travel a distance d is:

$$\text{time} = \frac{d}{v} = \frac{1}{H_o}$$

Therefore, the value of $\dfrac{1}{H_o}$ gives us an estimate of the age of the Universe.

This is only an estimate because as the galaxies in the time-reversed Universe fall towards one another, they would be expected to speed up.

So, assuming that the value of the H_o parameter is constant, the approximate age of the universe $= \dfrac{1}{H_o} = \dfrac{1}{2.4 \times 10^{-18}} = 4.17 \times 10^{17}$ s $= 13.2$ billion years.

Other methods of determining the age of the Universe suggest that it is slightly older than our estimate above.

The size of the universe

The absolute size of the universe is unknown, but there is an upper limit on the size of the observable universe. This upper limit is a sphere, with the Earth at its centre and with a radius equal to the distance that light could travel from the Big Bang until now. So if the age of the Universe is approximately 13.2 billion years, then the sphere has a radius of approximately 13.2 billion light-years.

Exercise 2.7

1   The siren mounted on a police car emits a sound of wavelength 50 cm. As the car approaches a stationary observer the sound detected by the observer has a wavelength λ_1. As the car travels away from the observer the sound detected has wavelength λ_2. The difference between these wavelengths is 6.8 cm. Given that sound travels in air at 340 m s^{-1}, calculate the constant speed of the car and the values of λ_1 and λ_2.

2   In an experiment a source of sound approaches a stationary observer at a speed of 100 m s^{-1}. The observer measures an apparent wavelength of 100 cm. The speed of sound relative to the observer is 350 m s^{-1}. Calculate the true frequency of the sound source.

3   A book on astronomy gives the value of the Hubble parameter, H, as 75.0 km s^{-1} Mpc^{-1}. This is because astronomers tend to measure speed in km s^{-1} and distances in mega parsecs. A parsec (pc) is 3.26 light years and a light year is 9.46×10^{15} m. Use these data to find the value of the Hubble parameter in s^{-1}, giving your answer to 3 significant figures.

4   In the laboratory, the wavelengths of the H-line and the K-line in the emission spectrum of calcium are 396.8 nm and 393.4 nm respectively. The wavelength of the H-line from a distant galaxy is found to be 19.8 nm greater than that in the laboratory.

(a) Calculate the wavelength of the K-line from this galaxy when it observed by an astronomer on Earth.

(b) Calculate the recession speed of the galaxy relative to the Earth.

Unit AS 3:
Practical Techniques and Data Analysis

3.1 Implementing

You should be able to:

3.1.1 Assemble and use measuring apparatus correctly, skilfully and effectively with full regard for safety, including:

- spring and top-pan balances (mass)
- rule, micrometer and callipers (length)
- graduated cylinder (liquid volume)
- clock and stopwatch (time)
- thermometer and sensor (temperature)
- ammeter (electric current)
- voltmeter (potential difference)
- protractor (angle)

(Note: digital versions of the apparatus are acceptable)

3.1.2 Make and record sufficient relevant, reliable and valid observations and measurements to the appropriate degree of precision and accuracy, using data loggers where suitable

3.1.3 Show familiarity with analogue and digital displays

Physics relies on accurate measurements of physical quantities such as mass, length, time and temperature. To improve the accuracy and precision of such measurements instruments such as metre rules, vernier callipers, stop clocks and thermometers are used. It is important that you know how to use these devices properly.

In measuring any quantity there is always some degree of uncertainty. Appreciation of the uncertainty associated with each measuring instrument is equally important. In this book the uncertainty in a reading will be taken as ± ½ the smallest division shown on the scale of the measuring instrument. However, it is equally acceptable to take the uncertainty in a reading as ± the smallest division on the scale.

Measuring length

Using a metre rule

Although this may be one of the simplest length measuring instruments to be found in a school laboratory, care must be taken with its use to avoid errors.

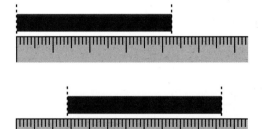

This is bad practice. The end of the metre rule may be worn giving rise to a zero error and an inaccurate measurement of the length.

It is good practice to place the metre rule against the object so that you have two readings to take.

Subtracting them will give you the length of the object. It avoids a zero error in the measurement. Of course the measurement of length still has an uncertainty associated with it.

The smallest division on the metre is usually 1 mm. If we say that each reading of the metre rule has an uncertainty of ± 0.5 mm then subtracting the two readings to obtain the length has an associated uncertainty of ± 1 mm.

For example, if the two readings are 14.0 cm and 56.5 cm, the length is 42.5 cm and if we quote the length with the associated uncertainty then we would write this as (42.5 ± 0.1) cm, i.e. an uncertainty in the length of about 0.25%.

For lengths greater than 1 m it is better to use a tape measure, with 1 mm divisions. Tape measures can be used to measure distances up to several hundred metres with good accuracy.

Parallax error

Parallax error occurs when any scale is not viewed at right angles (or **normally**) as shown. Failure to view the scale at right angles will give a reading which is either too high or too low.

Having the scale of the metre rule as close as possible to the object will reduce the possibility of a parallax error.

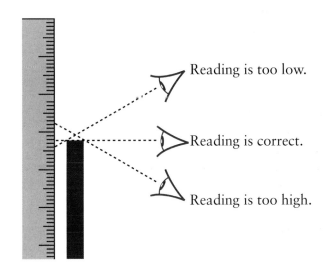

Reading is too low.

Reading is correct.

Reading is too high.

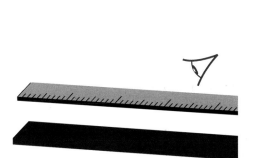

The object to be measured is too far from the scale increasing the possibility of parallax error.

Moving the object closer to the scale as shown is good practice since it reduces the possibility of parallax error.

Vernier calliper

The vernier calliper is a precision instrument that can be used to measure internal and external distances extremely accurately. The example shown below is a manual calliper. Measurements are interpreted from the scale by the user.

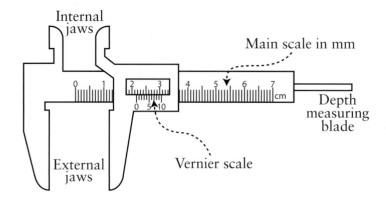

The internal jaws can be used to measure the internal diameter of, say, a tube, and the external jaws can be used to measure the external diameter of a tube or the width of a block. The depth measuring blade can be used to measure the depth of, say, a hole drilled in a metal bar.

The calliper in the diagram below can read to ± 0.1 mm. To take the reading you should follow the two steps shown below.

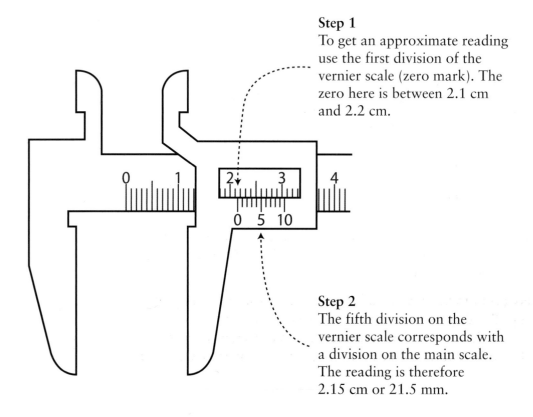

Step 1
To get an approximate reading use the first division of the vernier scale (zero mark). The zero here is between 2.1 cm and 2.2 cm.

Step 2
The fifth division on the vernier scale corresponds with a division on the main scale. The reading is therefore 2.15 cm or 21.5 mm.

Exercise 3.1A

Work out the following readings.

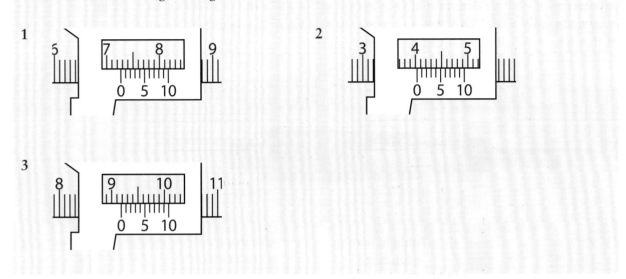

Digital (vernier) calliper

An increasing number of schools are now using digital vernier callipers like the one shown in the diagram below. Just like the manual type, a digital calliper can be used to measure internal and external distances extremely accurately.

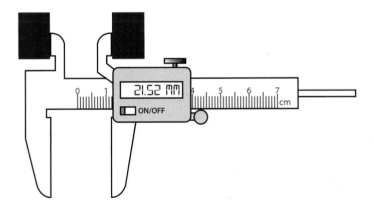

The measurement is shown on a LCD display. The parts are the same as those on the manual type, the only addition is an on/off switch for the LCD to extend the life of the small battery used to power it.

The digital display needs to be set to zero before it can be used to measure a distance accurately. The display is turned on and the external jaws are brought together until they touch. The zero button should then be pressed. This procedure should be followed when turning on the digital calliper for the first time.

Using a micrometer gauge

A micrometer gauge can measure distance to an accuracy of ± 0.01 mm. It is particularly useful for measuring the diameter of a wire or the thickness of a glass microscope slide. The area of a wire can be calculated when the diameter of the wire is measured using a micrometer gauge.

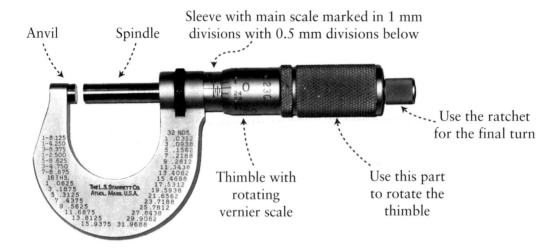

Anvil   Spindle   Sleeve with main scale marked in 1 mm divisions with 0.5 mm divisions below

Thimble with rotating vernier scale

Use this part to rotate the thimble

Use the ratchet for the final turn

The divisions along the micrometer are 1 mm. There are 50 divisions around the barrel of a micrometer normally used in schools.

To move the thimble 1 mm along the barrel requires the thimble to be moved through 2 complete turns. There are 50 divisions around the thimble, so to move 1 mm the barrel is turned 100 divisions. This means that 1 division around the barrel = 0.01 mm

The top scale gives a reading between 7.0 and 7.5 mm. (Note that the 0.5 mm division on the lower scale is not all visible in this image.)

On the vernier scale, division 38 lines up with the main scale. This is 0.38 mm. The complete reading is therefore 7.38 mm.

Exercise 3.1B

Work out the following readings.

1

2

3

Measuring volume

Using a graduated cylinder

Graduated cylinders are used to measure the volume of a liquid. They come in a range of sizes from 10 cm³ to 1000 cm³. Liquids in glass containers curve at the edges; this curvature is called the **meniscus**. With water in glass, the meniscus will curve up at the edges and down in the centre so we say you read the bottom of the meniscus. When reading the volume you should have your eye level with the meniscus of the liquid to avoid parallax error. In some plastic cylinders water has a flat surface. However, it is still best to take the reading at the centre rather than at the edge.

The visibility of the meniscus can be improved by using a card with a dark stripe on it, placed behind the cylinder. Adjusting the position of the card you will either see a white meniscus against a black background or a black meniscus against a white background. There are some liquids where the curve goes the other way. In this case you would take the reading at the top of the meniscus.

Like most measuring instruments, it is important to work out the volume represented by each of the marked divisions.

The volume of an irregular object such as a stone can be found using the displacement method. In this technique a graduated cylinder is partly filled with water and the volume measured. The stone is carefully lowered into the water and when completely covered with water the new volume is measured. The difference between the two readings gives the volume of the stone.

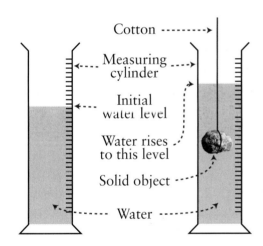

The method can be adapted to find the volume of an object that floats, like a cork. The stone is tied to the cork and, provided both are completely covered, the volume of the cork can be found.

Measuring weight – using a spring balance or Newton meter

This is used to measure force. It consists of a spring which extends when a force is applied to one end. The spring obeys Hooke's law, so the extension produced is proportional to the force. This allows a scale calibrated in newtons to be placed alongside the spring.

The maximum force that can be measured depends on the strength of the spring. Spring balances with ranges of 0–10 N, 0–20 N and 0–50 N are common.

Measuring mass – using an electronic top-pan balance

This is used to measure the mass of an object. The object is placed on the pan and the force it exerts is detected by a sensor which converts this to an electrical signal. A conversion factor is applied and the display will show the mass of the object in grams or kilograms.

Most electronic balances have a 'tare' facility. When pressed this sets the reading to zero. This is useful when measuring a required mass of a solid or liquid in a beaker or other container.

The container is placed on the pan, the tare button is pressed and the reading goes to zero. The reading then shown is the mass of material added to the container.

The final decimal place indicates the uncertainty. For the electronic balance shown this is ± 0.1 g.

Measuring angles – using a protractor

Notice that numbers marked on the protractor run in both directions, so be careful which you use when taking measurements.

To measure the angle between two lines follow the steps below:

- Find the centre of the straight edge of the protractor. This is the cross as shown below.
- Place the cross over the point of the angle you wish to measure or draw.
- Line up the zero on the straight edge of the protractor with one of the sides of the angle or the line already drawn.
- Find the point where the second side of the angle intersects the curved edge of the protractor (you may need to extend the lines). The value at the intersection is the measure of the angle in degrees.

There is of course uncertainty associated with the measurement of this angle. The reading on the scale can be read to ± ½ of one division. This corresponds to ± 0.5°. The positioning of the line along the zero of the protractor also involves an uncertainty of ± ½ of one division, again this is ± 0.5°.

The overall uncertainty in the measurement of the angle is ± 1°.

The angle shown in the diagram should be quoted as (33 ± 1)°.

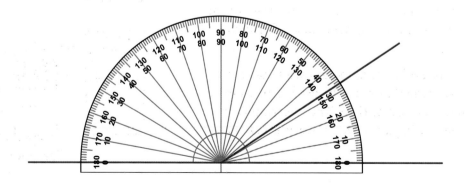

Measuring temperature

In Physics we use the Kelvin and the Celsius temperature scale. On the Celsius scale water freezes at 0°C: on the Kelvin scale this is 273 K. Water boils at 100°C or 373 K.

The thermometers found in school laboratories are normally calibrated from –10°C to 110°C. It is possible to get thermometers capable of measuring higher temperatures than 110°C.

It is important to determine the temperature difference indicated by the smallest division shown on the thermometer. This is normally 1°C, so it is possible to read the scale to ± 0.5°C. Therefore a temperature change would be measured to ± 1°C.

Thermometers are made of glass and therefore fragile. Most are round and they can easily roll off a bench. However, some are triangular in cross-section or have a small plastic triangle around them to reduce the likelihood of rolling.

When recording the temperature of a liquid it is important to stir the liquid to ensure thorough mixing. When heating a liquid do not use the thermometer to stir the liquid unless it is robust and clearly intended for the purpose. When recording the temperature of a liquid ensure than the bulb of the thermometer is completely covered by the liquid or is as close as possible to the position at which the temperature is to be measured.

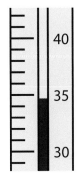

Smallest division: 1.0

Uncertainty: ± 0.5 °C

Reading: 34.5 °C

The example on the left shows how to measure temperature accurately using a thermometer.

Electronic thermometers and temperature sensors

Electronic thermometers and temperature sensors are recent replacements for liquid-in-glass thermometers.

The advantage of the electronic thermometer is the easily readable value displayed on a screen. The uncertainty in this instrument is ± the value of the last figure shown on the display. For the one shown on the right it is ± 0.1 °C.

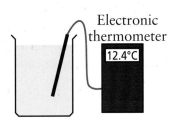

The temperature sensor is used in conjunction with computer software. It has the advantage that it can be used to measure and record temperature over a period of time. The uncertainty in temperature measurement using a typical sensor is ± 0.1 °C.

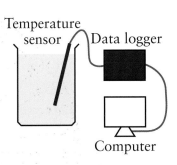

Measuring current – using an ammeter

An ammeter measures electric current. An ammeter is connected in **series** with the other components in a circuit. The positive terminal of the ammeter is connected to the positive side of the cell. If there are other components in the circuit you should trace the connections from the positive terminal of the ammeter to the positive terminal of the cell. The circuit below (left) shows an ammeter in series with a bulb.

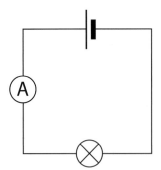 

The scale of an ammeter can measure amperes (A), milliamps (1 mA = 1×10^{-3} A) or possibly microamps (1 µA = 1×10^{-6} A). You should also determine what the smallest division of the scale represents. This is important when it comes to considering the uncertainty associated with a measurement of current. The uncertainty is normally taken as ± ½ the smallest division on the scale.

The ammeter shown above (right) is of a type found in many school laboratories. The top scale can measure currents up to a maximum of 1.0 A, the lower scale to a maximum of 5.0 A. The scale to be used is determined by which of the terminals, 1 A or 5 A, is used to connect the meter into the circuit.

Using the ammeter shown above, the top scale has the following features:
Maximum current is 1.0 A
Smallest division is 0.02 A
Uncertainty is ± 0.01 A (± ½ division)

Using the ammeter shown above, the bottom scale has the following features:
Maximum current is 5.0 A
Smallest division is 0.1 A
Uncertainty is ± 0.05 A (± ½ division)

The type of meter shown can easily be converted to a milliammeter by changing the shunt. The procedure outlined above can be used to determine which scale to use and the uncertainty associated with that scale.

Digital ammeters are also found in school laboratories. The one shown (right) can measure current as large as 10 amperes. The final decimal place indicates that the uncertainty associated with the use of this ammeter is ± 0.01 A.

Measuring potential difference – using a voltmeter

A voltmeter measures potential difference. It is connected in **parallel** with the component across which the potential difference is to be measured. The positive terminal of the voltmeter is connected to the end of the component which is nearest to the positive terminal of

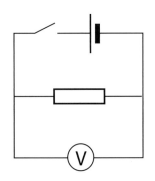
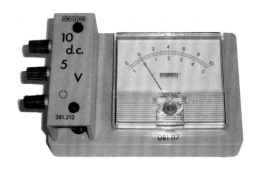

the cell, battery or power supply and the negative terminal to the other end of the component. When building a circuit the voltmeter can be the last item attached.

The voltmeter shown above (right) has a multiplier which allows the top scale to have a maximum reading of 10 V and the lower scale a maximum of 5.0 V.

Using the voltmeter shown above, the top scale has the following features:
Maximum current is 10.0 V
Smallest division is 0.02 V
Uncertainty is ± 0.01 V (± ½ division)

Using the voltmeter shown above, the bottom scale has the following features:
Maximum current is 5.0 V
Smallest division is 0.1 V
Uncertainty is ± 0.05 V (± ½ division)

Digital voltmeters are also found in school laboratories. The one shown on the right can measure a potential difference as large as 20 V.

The final decimal place indicates that the uncertainty associated with the use of this voltmeter is ± 0.01 V.

Zero error

When using a meter it is important that it reads zero before any current passes through it or a potential difference is applied to it. The one shown on the right has a zero error. It may be possible to set the pointer to read zero. If this cannot be done then the zero error value must be subtracted from all your readings.

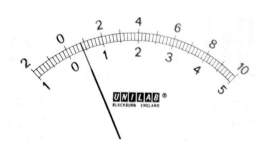

It requires skill to carry out an experiment well. Skill involves being able to manipulate equipment, identify variables that can be measured, varied and controlled, and take readings from a range of measuring instruments. To become a skilful experimenter requires practice but what follows is a number of simple techniques that can improve your experimental technique and lead to more precise measurements.

What is the difference between an accurate measurement and a precise measurement?

An accurate measurement is one that is close to the true value of a physical quantity. A precise measurement is one taken with a measuring device that can give an exact value when used with skill. For example, using a vernier scale that reads to 0.1 mm will give a more precise value than a metre rule that reads to 1 mm. Of course it requires more skill to take a reading with a vernier scale than with a metre rule. Measurements can be:

Precise and **accurate**
The measurements are close to the true value and the measurements are very similar, i.e. random and systematic uncertainties are small.

For example:
True value: 2.45
Readings taken: 2.42, 2.46, 2.44, 2.45
Average: 2.44

Precise but **inaccurate**
The measurements show very small differences but their average value is far from the true value.

True value: 2.45
Readings taken: 2.82, 2.84, 2.85, 2.87
Average: 2.85

Imprecise but **accurate**
The measurements show large variation but an average value that is close to the true value.

True value: 2.45
Readings taken: 2.82, 2.26, 2.72, 2.15
Average: 2.49

Imprecise and **inaccurate**
The measurements show large variations and an average value far from the true value.

True value: 2.45
Readings taken: 2.62, 2.76, 2.14, 2.95
Average: 2.62

What are systematic errors?

A systematic uncertainty will result in all readings being either above or below the accepted value. In other words it leads to inaccuracy of the measurement although the measurements taken may well be precise (very small differences between them). This uncertainty **cannot** be eliminated by repeating readings and then averaging.

Examples of systematic uncertainty are:

Zero error

Where appropriate, instruments should be checked for any zero error. Where there is a zero error, the instrument should be adjusted to zero or, if this not possible, the zero error should be noted and all recorded readings should then be adjusted.

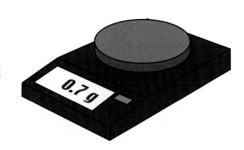

Note: Remember to record all readings as they are taken. Do not allow for zero error 'in your head' and then write down the adjusted value.

Parallax error

Parallax error occurs when the scale is not viewed normally when taking a reading. To reduce parallax errors, always:

- have the scale as close as possible to the pointer.
- view the scale normally.

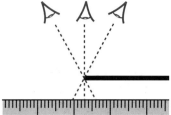

Reading too high   Correct reading   Reading too low

Over-tightening a micrometer

Over-tightening a micrometer gauge when taking a measurement will lead to a systematic error that will always give a smaller value than the true value.

Always use the ratchet for the final turn, because this will slip when the jaws meet any resistance. This is particularly important if you are measuring the diameter of a wire.

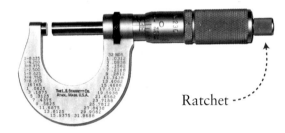

Ratchet -----

Techniques designed to improve the accuracy of your measurements

Timing oscillations

Start your timing when the oscillation is at one extreme, i.e. when the vibrating object is momentarily at rest. In the case of the simple pendulum shown on the right, one oscillation would be from C to A to B and back to C again. Start the object oscillating before you start timing and watch the object until the vibrations are no longer noticeable. This will determine how many oscillations are noticeable. When you decide to start timing, begin by saying zero as you start.

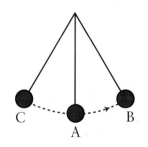

It is poor practice to measure the period by timing just 1 oscillation. The error in human timing is likely to be around 0.2 s. It is better to time 20 such oscillations, as this will reduce the uncertainty. However, in some circumstances the oscillations may die out quickly and only 3 or 5 complete oscillations may be noticeable. A simple pendulum with a period of just 1 second would have an error of 0.2 s, i.e. 20%. However, if you time 20 such oscillations the error is only 0.2 s in 20 seconds, i.e. 1%.

When you take measurements, vary the quantity in a logical manner, for example, increase the length of the pendulum in equal sized steps. This will allow trends to be more noticeable.

Measuring current and potential difference

Always draw the circuit diagram before you start building the circuit. Start at the positive terminal and insert components as you follow the circuit from positive to negative.

Voltmeters should be left until all the series components have been connected. Remember voltmeters are connected in parallel. Ammeters and voltmeters are always connected as positive to positive or red to red.

When using analogue meters establish what each division on the scale represents. When taking a reading, look vertically down on the scale (at a right angle). This reduces the possibility of parallax error in your reading. If you are using a digital meter, do not change the scale in the middle of the experiment.

In many cases try to change the potential difference in equal steps. However, when dealing with light emitting diodes (LEDs) it may be necessary to change the potential difference in very small steps when the current is beginning to increase.

3.2 Analysis

You should be able to:

3.2.1   Present work appropriately in written, tabular, graphical or other forms

3.2.2   Analyse, interpret and explain their own and others' experimental and investigative activities, using ICT and other methods

3.2.3   Show awareness of the limitations of experimental measurements when commenting on trends and patterns in the data

3.2.4   Draw valid conclusions by applying knowledge and understanding of physics

The first step in the analysis of your data is the recording of measurements in a suitable table. The table should have sufficient columns for all the measurements and possible calculations you need to make.

Columns need headings. These should state the quantity and the appropriate units for that quantity.

Below is an example of a table that could be used for the investigation of the period of a simple pendulum and the length of the pendulum.

Measurement repeated three times to give an average

Units shown on all column headings

Systematic and a good range

Length of the pendulum / m	Time for 20 oscillations / s			Average time for 20 oscillations / s	Period / s
	1st	2nd	3rd		
1.2					
1.0					
0.8					
0.6					
0.4					
0.2					

The length is varied in a systematic manner: it is gradually increased in length using steps of 0.2 m. Increasing the length from 0.2 to 1.2 m covers a good range of values. For each length the time for 20 oscillations is measured. To improve the accuracy and ensure reliability, this is done 3 times and the average taken. The final step is to calculate the period of the pendulum by dividing the average time by 20.

The measurements could be entered into a spreadsheet to process the data and present it in a form suitable for use in graph plotting software. However, it is essential that you develop your own graph plotting skills, as these will be required in any practical examination.

To reduce the uncertainty in the measurement of the periodic time of any vibrating system, it is advisable to time sufficient oscillations so that a total time of around 20 seconds or better is to be measured. In the case on page 183, a pendulum with length of 0.2 m would yield around 18 seconds and the length of 1.2 m would yield a total time of around 40 seconds.

However, it is not always possible to obtain sufficient oscillations to achieve a total time of at least 20 seconds. In this case you need to determine the maximum number of oscillations that you can detect before they cease to be noticed.

AS Practical

In this a bifilar pendulum was set up for you. The pendulum was made to vibrate about its centre. The length of the vertical cords was to be varied and the effect this had on the periodic time of oscillation was to be investigated.

The timing was to be carried out using a stopwatch or stopclock. The length of the supporting cords was to be decreased from 400 mm to about 200 mm and 5 sets of readings were to be taken.

The results were to be recorded in a table that was partly completed with the first value of L and the period T column shown with the appropriate unit.

When the bifilar pendulum was set swinging it was found that 5 oscillations were easily observable. More than this and they became very difficult to see. As you can see from the table, it was decided that 5 oscillations should be timed.

L / mm	Time for 5 oscillations / s				T / s
	1st	2nd	3rd	Average	
400	9.55	9.40	9.51	9.48	1.90
350	8.90	8.85	8.82	8.85	1.77
300	8.21	8.30	8.25	8.25	1.65
250	7.35	7.51	7.53	7.46	1.49
200	6.52	6.75	6.62	6.63	1.33

The relationship between T and L is given by one of the following equations. Which one?

$$1 \quad T = A\sqrt{L} \qquad 2 \quad T = \frac{A}{\sqrt{L}} \qquad 3 \quad T = \frac{A}{L^2}$$

From the trend shown by the results it is clear that **1** is the correct relationship. As the length L increases the period T also increases. Equations **2** and **3** indicate that as L increases T would decrease.

To draw a suitable straight line graph from the results to find the constant A then $\sqrt{L}$ should be plotted on the x-axis and T on the y-axis. A new table containing the appropriate values is then produced.

$\sqrt{L}$ / mm$^{\frac{1}{2}}$	14.14	15.81	17.32	18.71	20.0
T / s	1.33	1.49	1.65	1.77	1.90

The graph obtained using these values is shown below.

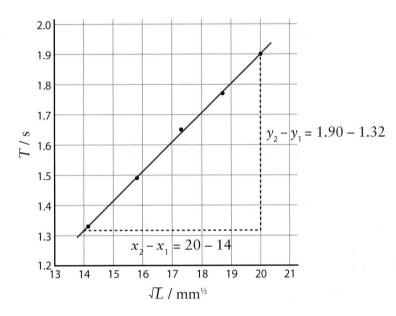

To find the value of A we need to take the gradient of this line. Why?

The relationship between L and T is given by $T = A\sqrt{L}$. This corresponds to $y = mx$, the equation for a straight line that passes through the origin $(0,0)$. Note that in this case there is no requirement to find the intercept so there is no need to plot the graph from the origin.

By comparing the two equations we see that $y \equiv T$ $x \equiv \sqrt{L}$ and the gradient $m \equiv A$.

The gradient $= \dfrac{y_2 - y_1}{x_2 - x_1} = \dfrac{1.90 - 1.32}{20.0 - 14.0} = \dfrac{0.58}{6.0} = 0.097$

The gradient may have units and in this case it has the units of s mm$^{-\frac{1}{2}}$.

Graphs

Graphs are commonly used to show the results of experiments. Graphs allow you to deduce relationships much more quickly than using a table. They provide a visual picture of how two quantities depend on each other: they show up anomalous readings and, if straight lines, the gradient can be used to find an average value of the ratio of the two quantities.

Dependent and independent variables

Plot the independent variable (the one you have been changing) along the horizontal axis and the dependent variable along the vertical axis. The exception to this rule occurs where you need to plot a particular graph to find a required quantity. For example, in the case of stretching a spring, the equation $F = kx$ applies. F is the force, x is the extension and k is the spring constant. In this instance F is the independent variable but to find the spring constant, the force F is plotted along the y-axis and the extension along the x-axis, because the gradient is then the spring constant.

Labels and units

Label both axes to show the quantity that is being plotted. Indicate on the axes the unit of measurement used for the quantity. Sometimes the quantity may just be a number so a unit is not required.

Scales

Choose scales on the axes to make the plotting of values simple. Generally this means letting 10 small divisions on the graph paper equal 1, 2, 5, 10 or some multiple of these numbers. Do not make life difficult for yourself by letting small divisions equal 3 or 7. This will take you longer to plot the graph, increase your chances of mis-plotting points and makes it difficult for others to read the data.

Choose the range of the scales on the axes so that the points are spread out. As a general rule the graph you draw should fill at least three quarters of the graph paper grid in both the x and y directions.

Plotting points

Plot the results clearly, and use a sharp pencil rather than a pen. Pencil is much easier to erase should you make a mistake in plotting. Use crosses or dots with circles around them.

Lines and curves

The graphs that you will encounter during an A level course will generally represent a smooth variation of one quantity with another, so a smooth curve or straight line will be appropriate. Draw a best fit line, which may be a smooth curve or a straight line that passes through or close to all your points as shown below. In general you should **not** join the points with short straight lines.

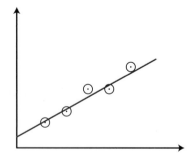 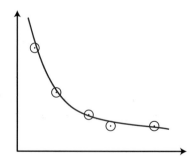

Worked Examples

1 A ball rolls from rest down a sloped plane. Measurements are made of the distance travelled along the slope, d, and the time taken, t.

The relationship between d and t is: $d = \frac{1}{2}at^2$ where 'a' is the acceleration of the ball.

(a) What **straight line** graph would you plot to display your results?

(b) How could you find the acceleration from the graph?

Solution

(a) The equation of a straight line that passes through the origin (0,0) is $y = mx$. By comparing this with the relationship above we see that d should be plotted on the y-axis and t^2 on the x-axis.

(b) In the equation for the straight line m represents the gradient. The gradient of the graph of d against t^2 is equal to $\frac{1}{2}$a.

2 The unknown e.m.f. of a cell, E, is linked to the terminal voltage, V, and the current, I, by the equation $E = V + Ir$ where r is the unknown internal resistance of the cell.

In an experiment, corresponding values of V and I are recorded as the resistance in an external circuit is changed. The e.m.f. and the internal resistance are both constant.

(a) What **straight line** graph would you plot? Which variable would be on the vertical axis?

(b) Draw a sketch of the graph you would expect to obtain.

(c) How would you find the e.m.f. of the cell and the internal resistance from this graph?

Solution

(a) First the equation has to be arranged so that V becomes the subject of the equation. This gives $V = E - Ir$. The equation of a straight lines is $y = mx + c$. By comparing these two equations we see that V should be plotted on the y-axis and I on the x-axis.

(b)

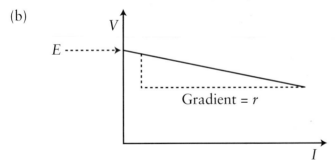

Gradient = r

(c) The intercept on the y-axis is c and in this case it will give us a value for E. The gradient of the graph is negative and will give a value for r.

3 The focal length *f*, of an inaccessible lens (inside a cylinder) can be found by a technique called 'the displacement method'. The distance between an illuminated object and a screen is measured, this is *s*, as shown in the diagram. The cylinder containing the lens is moved until a sharp image is obtained on the screen. The position of the cylinder is noted. The cylinder is moved again until a new image on the screen is obtained. The distance between the two positions of the cylinder containing the lens is found, this is *d*, as shown in the diagram.

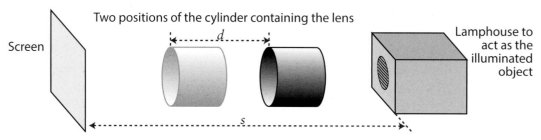

The mathematical relationship between the quantities is $f = \dfrac{s^2 - d^2}{4s}$

Below is a table of results of *s* and *d*.

s / cm	50.0	54.0	58.0	62.0	66.0	70.0
d / cm	22.4	27.5	32.3	36.9	41.4	45.8

(a) What **straight line** graph should you plot so that the gradient can be used to calculate the focal length of the lens?

(b) Copy the table above and calculate the values required to plot the graph. Insert the values in the appropriate spaces in your table and add appropriate labels.

(c) Plot the graph, labelling carefully the units on each axis and use it to find the focal length of the lens.

Solution

Rearrange the equation to give:

$s^2 = d^2 + 4sf$

Divide both sides by s:

$s = \dfrac{d^2}{s} + 4f$

Plot s on the *y*-axis and $\dfrac{d^2}{s}$ on the *x*-axis. The intercept is equal to 4*f*.

Alternatively, rearrange the equation to give:

$4fs = s^2 - d^2$

$(s^2 - d^2) = 4fs$

Plot $(s^2 - d^2)$ on the *y*-axis and *s* on the *x*-axis. The slope is 4*f*.

3.3–3.5 Evaluation, Refinement and Communication

You should be able to:

3.3.1 Assess the reliability of data, results and conclusions drawn from the data

3.3.2 Evaluate the methodology used in and the impact of the experimental activity, and demonstrate an appreciation of their limitations

3.3.3 Calculate the absolute and percentage uncertainty in a quantity

3.4.1 Suggest improved effective and safe procedures, after considering quantitative and qualitative methods

3.4.2 Modify procedures in response to serious sources of systematic and random error in order to generate results that are as accurate and reliable as the apparatus allows

3.5.1 Communicate observations, measurements, results and conclusions in an appropriate and effective manner

Reliability and methodology

When you evaluate the result of an experiment, the reliability of the data is of major concern. For the data to be reliable, the variation of the values must be small. There will always be some variation in any set of measurements.

In an experiment to measure a particular quantity, three experimenters (A, B and C) obtained the values shown in the table below. The accepted value for this quantity is 9.8.

A	B	C
Reliable but not valid	Not reliable and not valid	Reliable and valid
10.5, 10.7, 10.6, 10.4	8.3, 7.5, 6.0, 5.5	9.7, 9.8, 9.7, 9.9

In the set of data in column A, each measurement is only slightly different from the others but the results are not close to the accepted value, so the measurements are reliable but not valid. This set of data suggests that the experimental method was good since the results are reliable but their lack of validity would imply that there is a problem with the measuring equipment. Calibration of the equipment would possibly eliminate this problem. A systematic error (see page 193) would be a likely cause of data with this type of characteristic.

In column B the measurements are very scattered and the values are not close to the accepted value, so the measurements are not reliable and not valid. This indicates poor experimental procedure as well as a problem with the equipment.

In column C the results are repeatable, meaning that each time a measurement is taken it has approximately the same value, so the measurements are reliable and valid. Clearly the experimental procedure was good and the equipment correctly set up.

Uncertainties from graphs

The slope or gradient of a graph provides a means of determining an average value for a physical quantity. The intercept on either the x- or y-axis is dependent on the slope. A small change in the slope can produce a large change in the value of the intercept.

The points plotted may not all lie on a straight line. It may be necessary to judge the best fit line. The slope of the best fit line will give you the best value for a physical quantity and the intercept on the appropriate will give you the best value for this quantity. The placing of this line of best fit can be aided by calculating the average x value and average y value, and plotting this point. This is known as the **centroid** and the line of best fit is drawn so that it passes through this point.

To estimate the uncertainty in the slope and the intercept, follow the procedure outlined below:

1 Draw the line of best fit as outlined above.

2 Now draw two more lines, one of maximum slope and one of minimum slope through the plotted points. The gradients of these two lines will give you a maximum and minimum value for the slope. The difference between these two values gives you a range and the uncertainty can be taken as half the value of the range.

3 Similarly the line of best fit will give best value for the intercept. The range of the intercept values can be found from where the lines of maximum and minimum slope cut the appropriate axis. The uncertainty in the intercept value is again half the range.

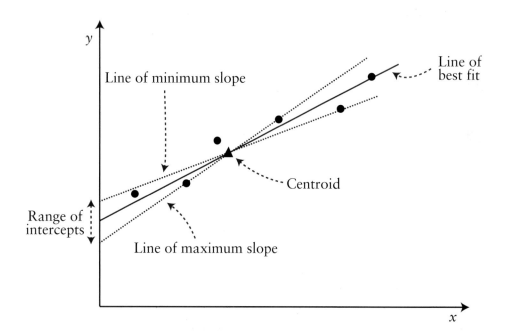

Combining uncertainties

Often the aim of an experiment is to find the value of a quantity that depends on the measurement of several quantities, each with its own associated uncertainty.

In an experiment to determine the resistivity of a material, the diameter of a wire is measured. Then that value is used to calculate the area of cross-section of the wire. What is the uncertainty in the calculation of the area of cross-section? There are two methods of dealing with this.

Method 1: Maximum, minimum and range

In this method the first thing to do is calculate the area using the best value of the diameter and the maximum and minimum values as determined by the measuring instrument. The average diameter of the wire was measured as 0.32 mm using a micrometer gauge, giving an uncertainty of $\pm$ 0.01 mm.

$$A_{\text{Best}} = \frac{3.142 \times (0.32 \times 10^{-3})^2}{4} = 8.0 \times 10^{-8} \text{ m}^2$$

$$A_{\text{Min}} = \frac{3.142 \times (0.31 \times 10^{-3})^2}{4} = 7.55 \times 10^{-8} \text{ m}^2$$

$$A_{\text{Max}} = \frac{3.142 \times (0.33 \times 10^{-3})^2}{4} = 8.55 \times 10^{-8} \text{ m}^2$$

This gives a range of 1.0×10^{-8} in the values for the area. The calculated value for the area can be written as: $(8.0 \pm 0.5) \times 10^{-8} \text{ m}^2$.

Method 2: Combining percentage uncertainties

Consider a measured quantity A and its associated uncertainty ΔA, and another measured quantity B with its associated uncertainty ΔB. X is the quantity we wish to measure and its uncertainty is ΔX. The value of X may be found by combining the values of A and B in various ways. For each way that A and B could be combined, the final uncertainty ΔX is simply the sum of the uncertainties in A and B. This is a simplified version of a statistical method that is applicable to AS and A2 Physics.

How X is found from A and B	Final uncertainty in X
$X = A \times B$	$\Delta X = \Delta A + \Delta B$
$X = A \div B$	$\Delta X = \Delta A + \Delta B$
$X = A \times B^n$	$\Delta X = \Delta A + n\,\Delta B$
$X = A \div B^n$	$\Delta X = \Delta A + n\,\Delta B$
$X = kA^n$ where k is a constant	$\Delta X = n\,\Delta A$

The uncertainties, ΔA and ΔB, are best quoted as percentages of the measured values A and B. The uncertainty ΔX is then a percentage of the final measured value.

For example, if the period of an oscillating pendulum is 1.1 s with an uncertainty of $\pm$ 0.1 s, the percentage uncertainty in this measurement is $(0.1 \times 100) \div 1.1 = \pm 9\%$

The examples below show how the rules shown in the table are applied.

Example 1: Measurement of resistance

The resistance of a length of wire is found by measuring the current passing through it and the potential difference across it. In such an experiment the values of these quantities and their uncertainties were found to be $V = 5.2 \pm 0.2$ and $I = 1.2 \pm 0.1$.

$$\Delta V = \frac{0.2 \times 100}{5.2} = 3.8\% \quad \Delta I = \frac{0.1 \times 100}{1.2} = 8.3\%$$

$$R = \frac{V}{I} \quad \Delta R = \Delta V + \Delta I = 3.8\% + 8.3\% = 12.1\%$$

$$R = \frac{5.2}{1.2} = 4.3 \ \Omega \pm 12.1\% = (4.3 \pm 0.5) \ \Omega$$

Example 2: Measurement of density

The diameter of a steel ball was measured using a micrometer gauge and found to be 8.65 mm, and the uncertainty was $\pm$ 0.01 mm. The mass of the steel ball was found using an electronic balance, the measured value being 2.82 g with an uncertainty of $\pm$ 0.01 g. What is the density of the steel?

The volume of the sphere is given by $\frac{\pi d^3}{6}$, d being the diameter of the sphere.

The uncertainty in the measurement of the diameter is:

$$\Delta d = \frac{0.01 \times 100}{8.65} = \pm 0.12\%$$

However, the uncertainty in the volume ΔV is three times this, since diameter has to be cubed to find the volume.

The uncertainty $\Delta V = \pm 0.36\%$

$$\text{Density} = \frac{\text{Mass}}{\text{Volume}} = \frac{2.82 \times 10^{-3}}{3.39 \times 10^{-7}} = 8318 \ \text{kg m}^{-3}$$

$\Delta m = 0.01 \times 100\% \div 2.82 = 0.35\%$

The uncertainty in the density ΔD
$= \Delta m + \Delta V = 0.35\% + 0.36\% = \pm 0.71\% = \pm 59 \ \text{kg m}^{-3}$

The final value for the density can be quoted as $(8318 \pm 59) \ \text{kg m}^{-3}$

Exercise 3.3A

1 In an experiment to measure the resistance of a piece of wire a voltmeter capable of measuring a maximum potential difference of 10 V was used. The smallest division on the scale was 0.2 V. The ammeter used was capable of measuring current as large as 1.0 A and the smallest division on its scale was 0.1 A. The experiment yielded readings of 4.9 V and 0.3 A. Calculate the resistance of the wire along with the uncertainty in its value. Use the percentage method to determine the uncertainty in the resistance.

Systematic and random errors – summary

Systematic errors in experimental observations will produce a result which is either above or below the accepted value. Taking a number of readings and finding the average will not minimise a systematic error. Improved experimental observation will reduce systematic errors.

Experimental technique can be improved in the following ways:
- View a scale at right angles. This avoids parallax error.
- If measuring the temperature of an object, ensure the thermometer is in good thermal contact with it. If measuring the temperature of a liquid, ensure it is well stirred before you begin.
- Ensure a meter reads zero when no current is flowing or potential difference is applied. This avoids zero error.
- If manually timing, start and stop the watch when the object is at a particular position. For example, in the case of a pendulum start and stop the timing when the pendulum bob is at the extreme of its motion and momentarily stopped.

Random errors in experimental measurements can be minimised by taking a number of readings of a quantity and finding the average. Drawing a graph and drawing the line or curve of best fit will also minimise the effects of random errors. When carrying out an experiment, always tabulate the measurements and calculate the average as discussed in the Analysis section (page 183).

The effect of random errors can be minimised in the following ways:
- If measuring the diameter of a wire, do this at several positions and at various angles along the length of the wire.
- If timing oscillations, for example, the period of a pendulum, time 10 or 20 oscillations and then find the average.
- If conducting an electrical experiment, measure the current as the voltage is first increased to the desired value then again as the voltage is decreased to the desired value. Calculate the average of the two currents.

Assessment of practical techniques and data analysis

Practical techniques and data analysis is assessed by two separate exam papers:

1 In **AS 3A**, you will be assessed on your practical skills by completing four short experimental tasks worth a total of 40 marks.

2 In **AS 3B**, you will be assessed on your analysis of experimental results worth a total of 50 marks.

Both AS 3A and AS 3B are externally assessed.

The following pages consist of examples of short practical tests and data analysis questions that should help prepare you for these assessments.

Assessment Unit AS 3A

In AS 3A, you will undertake four short tasks in 1 hour.

Exercise 3.3B provides a number of sample tasks, similar to those that you will encounter in the exam.

Exercise 3.3B

1 **Resistance of a filament lamp**

   (a) Considering the apparatus listed below, draw the circuit diagram you will use to collect the data from which you can determine the resistance of a filament lamp at different potential differences.

   Equipment list:
   - 12 V bulb
   - DC variable power supply 0 to 12 V
   - Voltmeter 0–12 V
   - Ammeter 0–3 A
   - Connecting leads

   (b) Set up the circuit and use it to obtain at least 5 values of the resistance of filament and corresponding voltage. Tabulate your results in an appropriate table with suitable column headings.

   (c) Sketch a graph to show how the resistance of the filament varies with the applied voltage.

2 Acceleration of free fall

The apparatus shown opposite has already been set up for you. The light gate is connected to a data logger.

The apparatus measures the time the light beam is interrupted by the opaque portion of the plastic strip. The time interval between the two opaque portions interrupting the beam is also measured by the apparatus.

You will drop the plastic strip from rest so that the opaque sections A and B break the light beam.

You should repeat this a number of times so that a reliable set of results are obtained.

Light gate

(a) Record your results in an appropriate table with suitable column headings.

(b) Apart from the times, what other measurement is required to calculate the acceleration of free fall?

(c) Use your results to calculate a value for the acceleration of free fall.

3 Measuring the focal length of a converging lens

The apparatus shown below has been assembled for you.

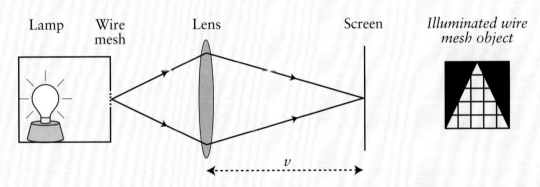

| Lamp | Wire mesh | Lens | Screen | *Illuminated wire mesh object* |

v

The convex lens can be moved so that a sharp image of the illuminated wire mesh is obtained on the screen.

You are asked to adjust the position of the lens so that at least three sharply focussed images are obtained on the screen.

(a) For each position, record the image distance v and calculate the magnification of the image. You should repeat the measurements a number of times and take an average.

(b) Record your measurements in an appropriate table with suitable column headings.

The magnification m, the image distance v and the focal length of the lens f are related by the equation:

$$m = \frac{v}{f} - 1$$

(c) Use the equation and your measurements to obtain a value for the focal length of the lens.

4 Measuring instruments

You are provided with the following measuring instruments.

- A 30 cm rule with the smallest division 1 mm
- A micrometer
- A vernier or digital calliper

Explain the procedure for calculating the volume and the % uncertainty for each of the following items:

(a) A steel ball bearing

(b) A glass microscope slide

(c) A CD

5 Principle of Moments

The apparatus below shows a metre rule pivoted at its mid point.

A Newton meter is attached at the 5 cm mark.

A weight W is able to be moved along the metre rule as shown.

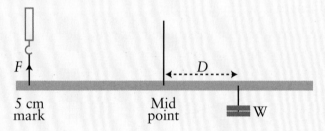

(a) Start with a weight of 2 N and move the weight W until the metre rule is horizontal.

When the metre rule is horizontal, record the reading F on the Newton meter and the distance D.

(b) Repeat this for 3 N and 4 N.

(c) Tabulate your results.

(d) Use your results to verify the Principle of Moments by presenting your calculations in an appropriate table with suitable column headings.

6 Measuring refractive index

The refractive index of glass can be measured using a triangular glass prism.

When a light ray passes through the prism it is deviated as shown in the following diagram (top of the next page).

The angle of deviation D is the angle between the incident ray and the emergent ray.

The angle of the prism is A.

The refractive index n is given by the equation:

$$n = \frac{\sin \frac{1}{2}(A + D)}{\sin \frac{1}{2}A}$$

Angle of incidence

(a) Measure the angle of the prism A.

(b) Measure the angle of deviation D for three angles of incidence. Use angles of 30°, 40° and 50°.

(c) Use your measurements to determine a value for the refractive index n.

Assessment Unit AS 3B

In AS 3B, you will be assessed on the analysis of experimental results. This is a separate exam paper from AS 3A and is worth a total of 50 marks. AS 3B is externally assessed.

Exercise 3.3C provides a number of sample tasks, similar to those that you will encounter in the exam.

Exercise 3.3C

1 In an experiment to measure the resistance of a piece of wire, a voltmeter capable of measuring a maximum potential difference of 10 V was used. The smallest division on the scale was 0.2 V. The ammeter used was capable of measuring current as large as 1.0 A and the smallest division on its scale was 0.01 A.

The experiment yielded readings of 4.9 V and 0.3 A.

Determine the percentage uncertainty in the voltage and current measurements, and in the calculated value of the resistance.

2 The circuit shown below (right) was used to investigate the electrical power dissipated in a resistor. The measurements taken are shown in the table below.

Potential difference / V	0	0.5	1.0	1.5	2.0	2.5	3.0
Power / mW	0	60	250	575	1000	1560	2250

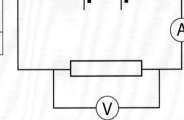

(a) Plot a suitable **linear** graph to verify that power is proportional to the square of the potential difference ie:

$$P = \frac{V^2}{R}$$

Before drawing the graph you will need to make a copy of the table above and add an extra row to allow you to calculate additional values.

Label this row with a suitable heading and units.

(b) Using the graph determine the value of the resistance R.

3 A ray of light passes through a rectangular glass block as shown below.

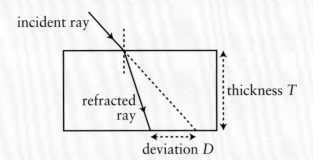

The deviation of the ray was measured as the angle of incidence was changed.

The results are shown in the table below.

Angle of incidence / °	10	20	30	40	50	60
Deviation / cm	1.3	2.4	3.9	5.6	7.7	10.2

(a) Plot a graph to show the results above. Draw the best fit curve through the points.
   Plot the angle of incidence on the x-axis and the deviation on the y-axis.

(b) The equation $D = 0.39 + 0.067i + 0.0015i^2$ approximately describes the curve you have drawn. D is the deviation in cm and i is the angle of incidence in degrees.
   Using an angle of incidence i of 45°, use this equation to calculate the deviation D.

(c) Calculate the percentage difference between this calculated value and the value obtained from your curve.

4 To measure the density of a stone the following steps were undertaken.

Its mass was measured using a digital balance. The mass of the stone was measured as 115 g. The digital balance had an accuracy of ± 2 g.

(a) Calculate the percentage uncertainty in the mass.

To find the volume of the stone the displacement of water in a measuring cylinder was carried out. The measuring cylinder was partly filled with water and the volume of water noted. This was 60 cm³. The volume of water was measured to an accuracy of ± 2 cm³.

(b) Calculate the percentage uncertainty in the volume of water.

The stone was then placed in the measuring cylinder so that it was completely covered. The reading was again noted. This was 130 cm³.

(c) Calculate the percentage uncertainty in the volume of water + stone.

(d) Calculate the volume of the stone and the percentage uncertainty in its volume.

(e) Calculate the density of the stone and its total percentage uncertainty.

(f) State the density of stone along with its absolute uncertainty.

5   A monochromatic ray of light was passed through a glass prism.

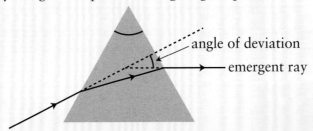

The angle between the incident ray and the emergent ray is known as the angle of deviation. The angle of deviation was measured for a range of angles of incidence. The results are shown in the table below.

Angle of incidence / °	45	46	47	48	49	50	51	52
Angle of deviation / °	39.5	39.4	39.3	39.3	39.4	39.5	39.6	39.7

(a) Plot a graph of angle of incidence (*x*-axis) against angle of deviation (*y*-axis).

(b) From the graph determine the minimum value of the angle of deviation.

(c) How might the experimental procedure be improved so that a more accurate value for the minimum value of the angle of deviation could be determined?

6   **Measuring the focal length of a lens**

A student measured the focal length of a converging lens by measuring object and image distances. He first of all used a distant object to measure an approximate value for the focal length of the converging lens.

(a) Explain how this measurement is useful when it comes to measuring object and image distances.

He drew a diagram of how he would arrange the apparatus and the measurements he would make. The diagram is shown below.

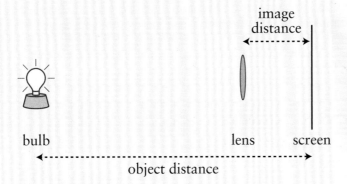

(b) What mistake has he made?

(c) When carrying out the experiment he found it difficult to focus the image of the bulb on the screen. What could he place in front of the bulb to make focusing easier?

7 When a ball bearing is dropped through a viscous liquid, such as syrup, the friction force is large and the ball bearing soon reaches its terminal velocity. In such an investigation the apparatus below (right) was set up. The time taken for each ball bearing to pass between two markers was measured a number of times and an average taken. This was carried out for a range of ball bearing radii.

Radius of ball bearing / mm	5	8	10	12	15
Average time / s	5.7	2.2	1.4	1.1	0.7

(a) Explain why it is important not to carry out the timings when the ball bearing is close to the top of the column of viscous liquid.

(b) Using the values shown above and the information from the diagram, determine the terminal velocity for the ball bearings of different radii.

(c) Which of the following expressions best agrees with your calculations?
   r = the radius of the ball bearing, v = terminal velocity and k = a constant
   A $v = kr$ B $v = k\sqrt{r}$ C $v = kr^2$

(d) Carry out the necessary calculations to support your answer to part (c).

20 cm

8 In an experiment to investigate the motion of a ball rolling down a slope, the apparatus below was set up. The time for the ball to move between two markers, 1.0 m apart, was measured a number of times. The results are shown in the table below.

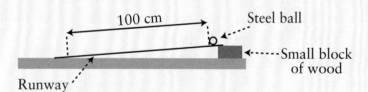

100 cm   Steel ball

Small block of wood

Runway

Height of the runway / cm	Time to travel 100 cm / s			Average time / s	Average speed / m s⁻¹	Final velocity / m s⁻¹	Acceleration
	1st timing	2nd timing	3rd timing				
2.5	5.0	5.2	4.9				
5.0	3.5	3.5	3.7				
7.5	2.93	3.01	2.8				
10.0	2.67	2.45	2.5				
12.5	2.23	2.31	2.20				

Make a copy of the table above.

(a) Calculate the average time for each of the runway heights used. Give your answer to two decimal places.

(b) Calculate the average speed of the ball for each of the runway heights used.

(c) Remembering that the ball started from rest, calculate the final velocity of the ball after it has travelled 1.0 m.

(d) Complete the table to show how the acceleration of the ball depended on the height of the runway. Include the appropriate unit for acceleration in the column heading.

(e) Based on the measurements taken, which of the following best describes the relationship between the acceleration of the ball and the height of the slope over the range of heights used.

$$\textbf{A}\ a = kh \qquad\qquad \textbf{B}\ a = kh^2 \qquad\qquad \textbf{C}\ a = \frac{k}{h}$$

Carry out sufficient calculations to justify your answer.

9 The reading on the ammeter shown in the circuit below was recorded as an increasing number of identical resistors are connected in parallel. The graph below shows the measurements taken. I is the reading on the ammeter and N is the number of resistors connected in parallel.

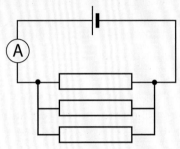

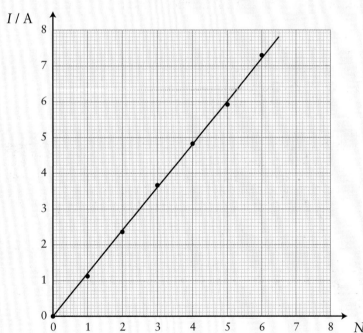

(a) Determine the gradient of this line, stating its unit.

(b) Using the graph, determine the value of one of these identical resistors.

(c) Deduce the linear equation for the relationship between I and N.

10 To measure the diameter of a steel sphere, a ruler and two wooden block are used as shown below.

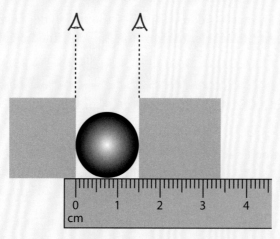

(a) Write down the diameter as shown and the percentage uncertainty in its measurement.

(b) Calculate the volume of the sphere and the percentage uncertainty in its value.

(c) The mass of the sphere was recorded as 15 g using a balance with an uncertainty of ±1.0 g. Determine the percentage uncertainty in the mass of the sphere.

(d) Calculate the density of the steel in the sphere and quote your answer with the value and the absolute uncertainty.

11 Measuring focal length

A student set up the apparatus below to determine the focal length of a convex lens.

She moved the object further from the lens and adjusted the lens distance from the screen until a sharp image was formed on the screen.

When a sharp image was obtained, the distance from the object to the lens was measured and the distance from the lens to the screen was also measured. The results are shown in the table below.

Distance to the object / cm	15	20	40	60	80	100	151	200
Distance to the screen / cm	30	20	13.3	12.0	11.4	11.1	10.7	10.5

(a) Plot a graph using the data in the table above.

(b) Use the graph to estimate the focal length of the lens and explain how you arrived at your answer.

Answers

Exercise 1.1

1. (a) joule: $kg\ m^2\ s^{-2}$ (b) watt: $kg\ m^2\ s^{-3}$ (c) $kg\ m\ s^{-1}$
   (d) $m\ s^{-2}$ (e) newton: $kg\ m\ s^{-2}$ (f) hertz: s^{-1}

2. FAT^2

3. The 2π term has no unit. The unit of $(L \div g)^{\frac{1}{2}} = (m \div m\ s^{-2})^{\frac{1}{2}} = (s^2)^{\frac{1}{2}} = s$, which is the unit of time on the LHS of the equation.

4. The 2π term has no unit. The unit of $(m \div k)^{\frac{1}{2}} = (kg \div N\ m^{-1})^{\frac{1}{2}}$
   Substituting the derived units for the newton gives: $(kg \div kg\ m\ s^{-2}\ m^{-1})^{\frac{1}{2}} = (s^2)^{\frac{1}{2}} = s$, which is the unit of time on the LHS of the equation. Since both sides have the same base units the equation is homogeneous.

Exercise 1.2

2. (a) 350 m   (c) 250 m 36.90 W of S
3. (b) 11.5°   (c) 10.2 m s^{-1}
4. 26.93 N, 58.7° (or 121.3°)
5. (a) 496 km (b) 112°

Exercise 1.3

1. (a) 1.03 N, 1.27 N   (b) Sum of upward reactions at C and D = Sum of downward forces.
2. (a) 425 N   (b) No   (c) equal to
3. (a) Reaction at C = 760 N, Reaction at D = 320 N   (b) 2.2 m   (c) 0.4 m
4. 270 N
5. (a) 0.7g or 6.9 N   (b) 0.7g or 6.9 N
6. 0.66 m

Exercise 1.4

1. A graph with time along the x-axis and velocity along the y-axis. The graph is a series of straight lines connecting the points (0,0), (2,1), (10,1), (12,0), (20,0), (22,–1), (25,–1) and (27,0).

2. (a) Measure gradient of tangent to curve at t_1.
   (b) 0, average velocity = average displacement $\div t_2$.

3. (a) 1.5 m s^{-2} (b) 186 m   (c) 10.3 m s^{-1}

4. (a) 6 m s^{-1} (b) –4 m s^{-1} moving to the left

5. (a) From $t = 0$ to $t = 3$ s, the ball is rising vertically. After $t = 3$ s, the ball is falling. The change in sign is due to the change in the ball's direction of motion.
   (b) 1.6 m s^{-2} (c) (i) 7.2 m above the surface (ii) 0 m   (d) (i) 7.2 m (ii) 14.4 m

6 (a) 20.26 m s^{-1} (b) Competitor A
7 (a) 1.01 m   (b) 0.26 m
8 (a) 22.2 m s^{-1} (b) 0.68 s   (c) 6.48 m s^{-2}
9 (a) speed = 0, acceleration = −9.81 m s^{-2} (b) 78.48 m   (c) 4 s
10 (a) 49.1 m s^{-1} (b) 24.6 m s^{-1} (c) 123 m
11 (a) 37.3 m   (b) 1.22 s   (c) 2.76 s   (d) 27.1 m s^{-1}
12 (a) velocity = +4.00 m s^{-1}, acceleration = −9.81 m s^{-2} (b) 22.8 m   (c) −21.2 m s^{-1} (d) 2.57 s

Exercise 1.5

1 (a) 60 m   (b) 44.15 m
   (c) Horizontal component = 20 m s^{-1}; vertical component = 29.4 m s^{-1} downwards.
   (d) 35.6 m s^{-1} at an angle of 55.8° below the horizontal.
2 (a) 1019 m (b) 25.9° and 64.1°
3 (a) Horizontal component $V_0 \sin \theta$. Vertical component $V \sin \alpha$.
   (b) Draw velocity-time graphs. The horizontal component of the velocity remains constant. The vertical component is a straight line beginning at a value of $V_0 \cos \theta$, and falling to a value of 0 at the highest point of the path, and then continuing below the x-axis until the ball reaches point A.
   (c) At its maximum height. Smallest speed = horizontal component only = $V_0 \sin \theta$.

Exercise 1.6

1 (a) 24.5 N   (b) 4.1 m s^{-2} (c) 8.2 m
2 (a) 12 m   (b) 8 m s^{-2} (c) 37 m
   (d) No. The child was 40 m away and the motorist stopped in 37 m.
   (e) Alcohol increases reaction time, so it increases stopping distance. Wet roads reduce friction and hence reduce the resultant force causing the car to stop. This reduces the deceleration and hence increases the stopping distance.
3 (a) 709 N   (b) 589 N   (c) 469 N
4 (a) 3 m s^{-2} (b) 600 N
5 (a) 1.96 m s^{-2} (b) 23.5 N
6 (a) Weight of 0.80g N acting downwards. A friction force of 1.5 N and an air resistance force of $0.16v^2$ N acting in the opposite direction to the direction of travel. A force of 5.5 N, due to the box being pushed, acting in the same direction as the direction of travel.
   (b) 5 m s^{-2} which occurs at the start of the motion.
   (c) This is the point when the total opposing forces (friction and the air resistance) are equal to the pushing force of 5.5 N, ie: $1.5 + 0.16v^2 = 5.5$, giving $v = 5$ m s^{-1}.

Exercise 1.7

1 (a) At maximum height horizontal velocity = $u \cos 60$ and vertical velocity = 0.
    So momentum before separation = $mu \cos 60$.
   (b) Part A has zero momentum. Part B has all the momentum equal to that before the explosion ie, $mu \cos 60$.

2 (a) Friction is a force external to the system of colliding bodies. The Principle of Conservation of Linear Momentum only applies in the absence of external forces. So to verify the principle for these colliding bodies, the track must be friction-free.
   (b) In an elastic collision kinetic energy is conserved. In an inelastic collision kinetic energy is not conserved.
   (c) Momentum before collision = Momentum after collision.
    $0.5 \times 0.18 = 2.0 \times v$, so $v = 0.045$ m s^{-1} to the right.
   (d) $a = \dfrac{\Delta v}{t} = \dfrac{(0 - 0.045)}{0.15} = -0.3$ ms^{-2}
    $F = ma = 2 \times (-0.3) = -0.6$ N
    The minus sign shows that the force is opposing the motion.

3 (a) Using conservation of momentum, Momentum of A = Momentum of B:
    $m \times v_B = 3m \times u$, giving $v_B = 3u$.
   (b) KE of A = $\frac{1}{2}\, 3mu^2$. KE of B = $\frac{1}{2}\, m(3u)^2$. So total energy = $6mu^2$.
   (c) Energy stored in the spring.

4 (a) See table on page 48.
   (b) $mu = mv + MV$ and $\frac{1}{2}mu^2 = \frac{1}{2}mv^2 + \frac{1}{2}MV^2$
   (c) $R = \dfrac{KE_{after}}{KE_{before}} = \dfrac{\frac{1}{2}mv^2}{\frac{1}{2}mu^2} = \left(\dfrac{v}{u}\right)^2 = \left(\dfrac{m-M}{m+M}\right)^2$
   (d) If $m = M$, $R = 0$ and both particles stop.
   (e) As $M \to \infty$, $R \to 1$
   (f) The best moderator has the least value of $\dfrac{v}{u}$:

    With carbon: $\dfrac{v}{u} = \left(\dfrac{m-M}{m+M}\right) = \dfrac{1-12}{1+12} = \dfrac{-11}{13}$ so, $v - 0.846u$

    With lead: $\dfrac{v}{u} = \left(\dfrac{m-M}{m+M}\right) = \dfrac{1-206}{1+206} = \dfrac{-205}{207}$ so, $v - 0.990u$

    So there is greater speed reduction with carbon than with lead. Hence carbon is a better moderator than lead.

Exercise 1.8

1 (a) 1.5 MJ   (b) 3.6 MW
2 (a) Increase in kinetic energy = $(\frac{1}{2} \times 1500 \times 5^2) - (\frac{1}{2} \times 1500 \times 15^2) = 1.5 \times 10^5$ J
    Increase in potential energy = $1500 \times 9.81 \times 500 \sin \alpha = 1500 \times 9.81 \times 33.3 = 4.9 \times 10^5$ J
   (b) Calculate the acceleration using $v^2 = u^2 + 2as$
    $a = 0.2$ m s^{-2} Resultant force $F_R = 1500 \times 0.2 = 300$ N
    Resultant force = Driving force – friction force – component of weight down the slope
3 (a) 5.10 m s^{-1} (b) 4.49 m s^{-1}

4 (a) Acceleration is not constant.

(b) From trigonometry, at the start the bob is 1 – cos 60 or 0.5 m vertically above lowest point.
½ mv^2 = mgh gives $v = \sqrt{9.81}$ = 3.13 m s^{-1}

5 (a) The student is correct, the total energy (PE + KE) is constant throughout and is ½mu^2.
At height h, PE = mgh, so KE = ½mv^2 = ½mu^2 – mgh
Giving $v = \sqrt{(u^2 - 2gh)}$ which is independent of projection angle α.

(b) Initial KE = ½m × 15^2 = 112.5m J
PE at 2.00m = mgh = m × 9.81 × 2 = 19.62m J
KE at 2.00m = 112.5m – 19.62m = 92.88m J
Using KE = ½mv^2 gives: $v = \sqrt{2}$ × 92.88 = 13.6 m s^{-1}

6 (a) See page 53   (b) 14.35 m s^{-1}

Exercise 1.9A

1 0.06 A or 60 mA

2 0.96 A

3 (a) 'Conventional flow' refers to the convention in Physics that current flows from the region of positive potential to that of negative or zero potential. However, in reality, in normal circumstances, the current in metals is entirely due to the flow of electrons in the opposite direction to that of the conventional current.

(b) 1.25×10^{15}

4 (a) 0.6 A   (b) 3.75×10^{18}

Exercise 1.9B

1 e.m.f. is the energy converted to electrical form when 1 C of charge passes through the battery (or e.m.f. is the pd across the battery terminals when it delivers zero current).

2 Charge = 5 C, Energy = 12 × 5 = 60 J

3 (a) Energy = QV = 1 × 9 = 9 J   (b) Energy = QV = 15×10^{-6} × 9 = 0.135×10^{-3} J

(c) Charge Q = It = 500×10^{-3} × 12 = 6 C. Energy = QV = 6 × 9 = 54 J

4 Charge Q = It = 50×10^{-3} × 2 × 60 = 6 C. Energy = QV; 24 = 6V, giving V = 4 V

Exercise 1.10

1 (a) See page 74.   (b) See page 75.

2 (a) The resistivity relates to the material and not the wire. The units are Ωm.

(b) If the wires were of the same diameter (area of cross-section) then the copper wire would be 5 times the length of the iron, but since its area is a quarter of the iron the length of copper wire would be ¼ of 5 = 1.25 m.

3 (a) Ohmic: current and potential difference are directly proportional.
Non-ohmic: current and potential difference not proportional.

(b) See I-V graphs on pages 67 and 69.

(c) The resistance is the ratio of the potential difference to the current.

4

Length / m	Voltage / V	Current / A	Resistance / Ω
0.10	0.50	0.36	1.39
0.20	0.90	0.33	2.73
0.30	1.00	0.24	4.17
0.40	1.20	0.22	5.45
0.50	1.50	0.21	7.14
0.60	1.70	0.20	8.50
0.70	1.90	0.19	10.0

The average diameter of wire = 0.318 mm
Area of cross-section = $\pi d^2 \div 4 = 7.94 \times 10^{-8}$ m^2
Plot a graph of resistance R (vertical axis) against length L (horizontal axis).
Gradient of the graph = $R \div L \approx 14.4$ Ωm^{-1} (calculated from the graph).
Resistivity ρ = gradient × area of cross-section = $14.4 \times 7.94 \times 10^{-8} = 1.14 \times 10^{-6}$ Ωm

5 (a) The two 4 Ω resistors in parallel have a total resistance of 2 Ω. The 10 Ω and 8 Ω in series
   with the parallel resistors gives a total of 20 Ω.

(b) The 5 Ω and 20 Ω (the original resistance of circuit 1) are in parallel:
$$\frac{1}{R} = \frac{1}{5} + \frac{1}{20} = \frac{5}{20}, \text{ so } R = \frac{20}{5} = 4\Omega$$

Exercise 1.11

1 The e.m.f. is the voltage measured across the terminals of a battery when **no current** is being drawn from it. The potential difference across the load resistance when a current is passing through it is known as the terminal potential difference.

2 (a) 0.67 Ω   (b) 3.27 A

3 $r = 1.5$ Ω, $E = 9.0$V

4 See graph on the right.
   Intercept is $E = 1.5$ V
   The gradient is $V \div I = -r = -1.0$
   Thus $r = 1.0$ Ω

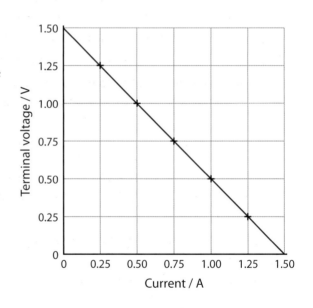

Exercise 1.12

1 $V = 12 \times (9 \div 20) = 5.4$ V

2 3.86 V and 1.0 V

3 (a) Since 6 V is across 10 kΩ, 3 V must appear across the unknown resistor. So, by proportion, unknown resistance = 3 × 10 ÷ 6 = 5 kΩ.

(b) When a voltmeter is connected and the slider is at the mid-point value of rheostat, the output voltage is across a combined resistance of 5 kΩ and 20 kΩ in parallel. This has a total resistance of (5 × 20) ÷ (5 + 20) = 4 kΩ.

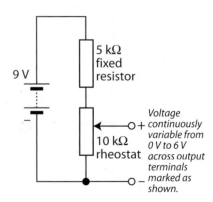

The voltmeter reading is therefore:

$V_{out} = R_1 V_{in} \div (R_1 + R_2) = (4 \times 9) \div (5 + 4)$

$V_{out} = 36 \div 9 = \mathbf{4\ V}$

4 (a) Total resistance = $V \div I = 3 \div 10 \times 10^{-6} = 300\ 000\ \Omega$

Output resistance = $V \div I = 1.2 \div 10 \times 10^{-6} = 120\ k\Omega$

Other resistance = $300\ k\Omega - 120\ k\Omega = 180\ k\Omega$

(b) Combined resistance of new 1.0 kΩ and 120 kΩ in parallel is 0.992 kΩ. So, output voltage is now across 0.992 kΩ, rather than 120 kΩ as before. This reduces output voltage from 1.2 V to 0.016 V and increases the current drawn from the battery from 10 µA to 16.6 µA.

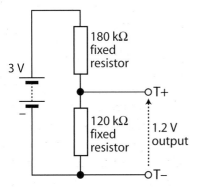

Exercise 2.1

1 (a) Gamma rays, X-rays, Ultra-violet, Visible, Infra-red, Microwaves, Radio

(b) 400 nm (violet) – 700 nm (red)

(c) An electric and a magnetic field oscillate at right angles to each other, and both oscillate at right angles to the direction in which the wave is moving. In the diagram on the right, the dark wave is the electric wave, light gray is the magnetic wave.

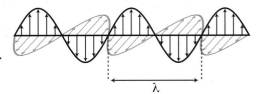

(d) Can travel through a vacuum or have associated oscillating electric and magnetic fields.

2 (a) Polarised waves are those in which the vibration is confined to a single plane.

(b) In unpolarised light there is an infinite number of planes of vibration, all of which are perpendicular to the direction of propagation. In sound waves, the vibrations are all parallel to the direction of propagation.

(c) Direct the laser light at a white screen. Introduce a piece of polaroid between the laser and the screen so that the laser light passes through the polaroid before reaching the screen. Turn the polaroid slowly through 360°. If the light is polarised there will be two positions where no laser light is seen on the screen; if the light is unpolarised this extinction is not observed.

3 (a) $T = \dfrac{1}{f} = \dfrac{1}{512} = 0.00195\ s = 1.95\ ms$ $\lambda = \dfrac{v}{f} = \dfrac{330}{512} = 0.645\ m$

(b) $v = 330 \times \sqrt{\dfrac{300}{273}} = 346\ m\ s^{-1}$

(c) $\lambda = \dfrac{v}{f} = \dfrac{346}{512} = 0.676\ m$

4 (a) $T = \dfrac{1}{f} = \dfrac{1}{5} = 0.2\ s$

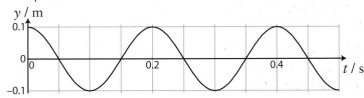

(b) $\lambda = \dfrac{v}{f} = \dfrac{20}{5} = 4\ m$

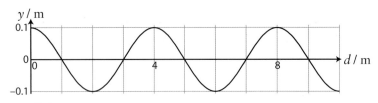

(c) $\phi = \dfrac{0.8}{4} \times 360° = 72°$

5 $\lambda = 5 \times 12 = 60$ cm = 0.6 m $v = f\lambda = 50 \times 0.6 = 30$ m s^{-1}

6 $T = \dfrac{\lambda}{c} = \dfrac{600 \times 10^{-9}}{3 \times 10^{8}} = 200 \times 10^{-17}$ s

   Number of waves in 2 *ns* = $2 \times 10^{-9} \div 2 \times 10^{-15} = 1\,000\,000$ waves

7 Period $T = 0.2$ s. Frequency $= \dfrac{1}{T} = \dfrac{1}{0.2} = 5$ Hz

8 (a) Amplitude = 32 ÷ 2 = 16 cm

   (b) Frequency $= \dfrac{v}{\lambda} = \dfrac{1.20 \div 0.6}{0.8} = 2.5$ Hz

9 (a) (i)

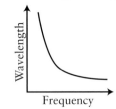

   (ii) A graph showing a horizontal line parallel to x-axis at 3×10^{8} m s^{-1}.

   (b) Since f = $c\lambda^{-1}$, the graph is a straight line through (0,0) with a gradient equal to the speed of light, *c*. So the gradient is 3×10^{8} m s^{-1}.

10 (a) Frequencies are the same.   (b) Wavelengths are the same.   (c) Speed is the same.

   (d) No information about the amplitude can be gleaned from the information given.

11 The amplitude is the maximum displacement of a particle from its equilibrium position.
   The frequency is the number of oscillations made in one second.
   The wavelength is the distance between two consecutive crests of a wave.
   The fourth statement ($fT = 1$) is correct.

Exercise 2.2

1 (a) For light of wavelength 589.3 nm the ratio of the sine of the angle of incidence in air to the sine of the angle of refraction in diamond is 2.419.

   (b) $c = \sin^{-1}(1 \div 2.419) = 24.4°$

   (c) At higher wavelengths the angle of refraction in diamond increases. So the refractive index at higher wavelengths is smaller than 2.419.

2 Angle of incidence in the glass = $\sin^{-1}(\sin 43 \div 1.40) = 29.2°$
   Critical angle = $\sin^{-1}(1 \div 1.40) = 45.6°$
   So increase in angle is $45.6° - 29.2° = 16.4°$

3 Angle of refraction in water = $\sin^{-1}(\sin 58° \div 1.33) = 39.6°$
   So angle $x = 58° - 39.6° = 18.4°$

4 (a) Graph is a straight line through the origin. Vertical axis labelled sin (i / °). Horizontal axis labelled sin (r / °).

(b) Refractive index is the gradient of the graph, which is approximately 1.32 (dependent on how the line of best fit has been drawn).

(c) $c = \sin^{-1}(1 \div 1.32) = 49°$ approx.

5 (a) $r = \sin^{-1}(\sin(75) \div 1.524) = 39.3°$

(b) Angle of incidence at BC = $90 - 39.3 = 50.7°$

(c) Critical angle = $\sin^{-1}(1 \div 1.524) = 41.0°$

Since the angle of incidence at BC is greater than the critical angle, the ray is totally internally reflected.

6 See text page 105.

7 (a) A step index fibre is an optical fibre consisting of a transparent core surrounded by a cladding. The core and cladding have a constant refractive index throughout; there is a sudden reduction in the refractive index as one moves from core to cladding.

(b) $_{cladding}n_{core} = \dfrac{1}{\sin c} = \dfrac{1}{\sin 60} = 1.1547$

(c) Speed of light in core = $3 \times 10^8 \div 1.6 = 1.875 \times 10^8$ m s^{-1}

Time to travel 500 m along axial path = $500 \div 1.875 \times 10^8 = 2.667$ μs

Suppose the axial mode distance corresponding to a single TIR is x. Then the corresponding distance at critical angle is $\dfrac{x}{\sin c} = \dfrac{x}{\sin 60} = 1.1547x$

Distance travelled in this mode = $500 \times 1.1547 = 577.35$ m

Time to travel this distance = $577.35 \div 1.875 \times 10^8 = 3.079$ μs

Time difference = $3.079 - 2.667 = 0.412$ μs

(d) (i) The engineer would want a cladding with a smaller refractive index so that C is larger and dispersion is reduced.

(ii) Increase the critical angle.

(iii) Reduces dispersion by reducing higher modes of propagation.

Exercise 2.3A

1 (a) (i) The image can be projected on to a screen and it is the same height as the object.

(ii) See text page 114 – object and image are both at 2F.

(b) (i) Diverging   (ii) Virtual

(iii) $u = \dfrac{v}{M} = \dfrac{25}{0.5} = 50$ cm

(iv) $\dfrac{1}{f} = \dfrac{1}{50} - \dfrac{1}{25} = -\dfrac{1}{50}$, so $f = -50$ cm $= -0.5$ m $P = \dfrac{1}{f} = \dfrac{1}{-0.5} = -2D$

2 (a) (i) and (ii) See text page 111.

(b) (i) $\dfrac{1}{u} + \dfrac{1}{v} = \dfrac{1}{f}$, so $\dfrac{1}{50} - \dfrac{1}{v} = \dfrac{1}{150}$ giving $\dfrac{1}{v} = \dfrac{1}{50} - \dfrac{1}{150} = \dfrac{2}{150} = \dfrac{1}{75}$. Hence $v = 75$ cm

Distance between object and image = $v - u = 75 - 50 = 25$ cm (since object and image are on same side of lens).

(ii) $M = \dfrac{v}{u} = \dfrac{75}{50} = 1.5$

(iii) Erect, virtual.

3 (a) (i) $\frac{1}{u} + \frac{1}{v} = \frac{1}{f}$ and, since the image is virtual, $\frac{1}{u} - \frac{1}{250} = \frac{1}{200}$

Hence $\frac{1}{u} = \frac{1}{200} + \frac{1}{250} = \frac{9}{1000}$ giving $u = 111.1$ mm. Then $M = \frac{v}{u} = \frac{250}{111.1} = 2.25$

(ii)

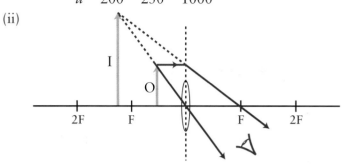

(b) (i) $\frac{1}{u} + \frac{1}{v} = \frac{1}{f}$ and, since the lens is diverging and the image is virtual, $\frac{1}{250} - \frac{1}{v} = -\frac{1}{200}$

Hence $\frac{1}{v} = \frac{1}{250} + \frac{1}{200} = \frac{9}{1000}$ giving $v = 111.1$ mm

Since the object and image are on the same side of the lens, the distance between them is $250 - 111.1 = 138.9$ mm

(ii) $M = \frac{v}{u} = \frac{111.1}{250} = 0.444$ and $h_i = M \times h_o = 0.444 \times 20 = 8.89$ mm

4 This is the displacement method for focal length. The easiest method is:

$f = (s^2 - d^2) \div 4s = (1250^2 - 250^2) \div (4 \times 1250) = 300$ mm

However, you can use an alternative solution using the lens formula:

First position: $\frac{1}{u} + \frac{1}{(1250 - u)} = \frac{1}{f}$

Second position: $\frac{1}{(u + 250)} + \frac{1}{(1000 - u)} = \frac{1}{f}$

Solving simultaneously gives $u = 500$ mm and $f = 300$ mm

5 (a–d) See text pages 116–117.

6 Focal length = 50 mm, $M = 1$

7 (a) $\frac{1}{u} - \frac{1}{v} = -\frac{1}{f}$, so $\frac{1}{u} - \frac{1}{40} = \frac{-1}{120}$ giving $\frac{1}{u} = \frac{1}{40} - \frac{1}{120} = \frac{2}{120} = \frac{1}{60}$. Hence $u = 60$ mm

(b) $M = \frac{v}{u} = \frac{40}{60} = \frac{2}{3}$

Height of image $= \frac{2}{3} \times$ height of object $= \frac{2}{3} \times 12 = 8$ cm

(c) Diminished, virtual, erect.

Exercise 2.3B

1 (a) Myopia

(b) Diverging lens, $f = -200$ cm

(c) $P = \frac{1}{f} = \frac{1}{-2} = -0.5$ D

(d) $\frac{1}{u} + \frac{1}{v} = \frac{1}{f}$, so $\frac{1}{u} - \frac{1}{25} = \frac{-1}{120}$ giving $\frac{1}{u} = \frac{1}{25} - \frac{1}{120} = \frac{7}{200}$.

Hence $u = \dfrac{200}{7} = 28.6$ cm = new near point with spectacles.

The range of vision is now 28.6 cm to infinity.

2 (a) See text page 122.

(b) Hypermetropia / long sight

(c) Converging lens

(d) $\dfrac{1}{u} - \dfrac{1}{v} = -\dfrac{1}{f}$, so $\dfrac{1}{25} - \dfrac{1}{150} = \dfrac{1}{f}$ giving $\dfrac{5}{150} = \dfrac{1}{f}$. Hence $f = 30$ cm

3 (a) Converging lens: $\dfrac{1}{25} - \dfrac{1}{70} = \dfrac{1}{f}$, giving $f = 38.9$ cm

(b) We need to find the location of an object giving a virtual image at 500 cm:

$\dfrac{1}{u} - \dfrac{1}{500} = \dfrac{1}{38.9}$, giving gives $u = 36.1$ cm, so the range is 25 cm to 36.1 cm

(c) Diverging lens, $f = -500$ cm

(d) We need to find the location of an object giving a virtual image at 70 cm:

$\dfrac{1}{u} - \dfrac{1}{70} = -\dfrac{1}{500}$ giving $u = 81.4$ cm, so the range is 81.4 cm to infinity

4 $M = \dfrac{v}{u} = \dfrac{18}{720} = 0.025$. But $h_i = M \times h_o = 0.025 \times 60$, hence $h_i = 1.5$ cm

Exercise 2.4A

1 (a) Vertical axis labelled Displacement / cm with numbers showing 1 cm per vertical division. Horizontal axis labelled Time / ms with numbers showing 5 ms per horizontal division, from 0 to 40 ms. As shown in part (b) below.

(b)

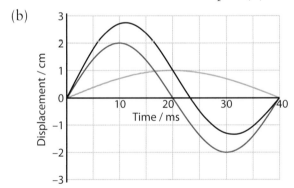

(c) Period of resultant wave = 40 ms. Frequency = $1 \div (40 \times 10^{-3}) = 25$ Hz

2 (a)

Progressive waves	Stationary waves
The disturbance produced in the medium travels onward, it being handed over from one particle to the next.	There is no onward motion of the disturbance. Each particle has its own characteristic vibration.
The amplitude of each particle is the same but the phase changes continuously.	The amplitudes of the different particles are different, ranging from zero at the nodes to maximum at the antinodes. All the particles between adjacent nodes vibrate in phase.

Table continued...

No particle is permanently at rest.	The particles at the nodes are permanently at rest but other particles reach their position of momentary rest simultaneously.
All the particles have the same maximum velocity when they pass through their mean positions.	All the particles have their own maximum velocity at the same time when they pass through their mean positions.
There is a flow of energy across every plane in the direction of propagation.	Energy is not transported across any plane.

(b) Two waves of the same amplitude, frequency and speed, and travelling in opposite directions superpose in space and time.

(c) A node is a point which is permanently at rest. An antinode is a point whose amplitude is a maximum.

3 (a) The sound is loudest.

(b) It is important that the resonance frequency is not below the starting frequency, so the initial frequency of the speaker must be low. The frequency is increased slowly to ensure that the resonance state is not missed.

(c) (i)   See text page 131.

(ii) $\lambda = L \times 4 = 30 \times 4 = 120$ cm $= 1.2$ m

(iii) $v = f\lambda = 280 \times 1.2 = 336$ m s^{-1}

(iv)   In the 2nd resonance position, $L = 0.75\lambda$, so $\lambda = 40$ cm.
New $f = v \div \lambda = 420 \div 0.4 = 1050$ Hz

4 (a) Distance between generator and pulley $= L = \lambda \div 2$
Wavelength $= 2L$ and $f = v \div \lambda = v \div 2L$

(b) Plot f / Hz (vertical axis) against L^{-1} / cm^{-1} (horizontal axis)

(c) Measure from the graph from part (b). Gradient is approximately 3600 cm s^{-1}.

(d) $v = 2 \times$ gradient $= 72$ m s^{-1} (approximately).

(e) No. The graph of f against L^{-1} is a straight line through the origin. So f is *inversely* proportional to L.

Exercise 2.4B

1 (a) The phase difference between the interfering waves is zero.

(b) The fringe brightness is a maximum.

2 (a) (i)   Monochromatic means light of a single wavelength (or frequency or colour).

(ii)   Coherent means same wavelength (or frequency) and constant phase difference.

(b) Candle flames emit light in random bursts, so their light cannot be coherent.

(c) Light is diffracted through the single slit, so light pulses arriving at the double slit are coherent.

3 (a) $\lambda = ay \div D = (400{\times}10^{-6} \times 3{\times}10^{-3}) \div 2.4$ m $= 500$ nm

(b) fringe separation $y = \lambda D \div a = (500{\times}10^{-9} \times 1.2 / 200{\times}10^{-6})$ m $= 3$ mm, so distance to the tenth fringe is 30 mm (as before).

4 (a) So that the sound at S_1 and S_2 is in the same phase.

    (b) On the axis of symmetry the path difference is zero. So the waves will interfere constructively.

    (c) S_1P must be bigger than S_2P, so the point P is on the vertical line, at the first bullet point *below* the axis of symmetry.

    (d) (i) 'fringe' separation $y = 0.60 \div 4 = 0.15$ m

         Then $\lambda = ay \div D = (0.30 \times 0.15) \div 1.2 = 0.0375$ m

      (ii) $v = f\lambda = 8000 \times 0.0375 = 300$ m s^{-1}

5 (a) The light from separate sources is emitted in random pulses and can therefore never be coherent.

    (b) (i) fringe separation is doubled   (ii) fringe separation is halved.

    (c) The 'light' is in the infrared part of the electromagnetic spectrum.

6 (a) Laser light is coherent. Without the single slit, the monochromatic sodium light is not coherent.

    (b) Although the fringes would now be further apart, they might be very faint.

Exercise 2.4C

1 Trombonists will be heard first. Low wavelengths will diffract more at the corner.

2 (a) Diffraction is the spreading out of waves as they pass through a small aperture.

    (b) (i) $d = \dfrac{1}{N} = \dfrac{1}{250} = 4\times10^{-3}$ mm = 4 µm

      (ii) $d \sin\theta = n\lambda$, so $\lambda = (4\times10^{-6} \times \sin(9.1°) \div 1) = 633$ nm

      (iii) $\sin\theta = \dfrac{n\lambda}{d} = 3 \times 633\times10^{-9} \div 4\times10^{-6} = 0.47475$, so $\theta = 28.34°$

         Angle between beams = $2 \times \theta = 2 \times 28.34 = 56.7°$

      (iv) maximum $n = \dfrac{d}{\lambda} = 4\times10^{-6} \div 633\times10^{-9} = 6.32$, so the highest order is 6.

3 $\sin\theta_1 = \dfrac{n\lambda}{d} = 2 \times 668\times10^{-9} \div 2\times10^{-6} = 0.668$, so $\theta_1 = 41.9°$

  $\sin\theta_2 = \dfrac{n\lambda}{d} = 2 \times 587\times10^{-9} \div 2\times10^{-6} = 0.587$, so $\theta_2 = 35.9°$

  So the angular separation is $41.9° - 35.9° = 6°$

4 (a) For the violet light, $d \times \sin\theta = n\lambda$

      $\theta = \sin^{-1}(3 \times 400\times10^{-9} \div 4\times10^{-6}) = 17.46°$

      So angular separation = $2 \times 17.46° = 34.9°$

    (b) For the orange light, $d \times \sin\theta = n\lambda$

      $\lambda = (4\times10^{-6} \times \sin 17.46°) \div 2 = 6\times10^{-7}$ m = 600 nm

Exercise 2.5A

1 (a) (i) 2.7 eV = $2.7 \times 1.6\times10^{-19}$ J = 4.32×10^{-19} J

      (ii) 2.7 eV is the smallest energy of an incident photon, which will just cause photoelectric emission.

      (iii) Energy of incident photon = $hf = \dfrac{hc}{\lambda} = 6.63\times10^{-34} \times 3\times10^8 \div 450\times10^{-9} = 4.42\times10^{-19}$ J, which is just greater than the work function. So photoelectric emission will occur.

(b)(i)   630 THz = 630×10¹² Hz = 6.30×10¹⁴ Hz

  (ii) $\frac{1}{2} mv_{max}^2 = hf - \Phi = 6.63 \times 10^{-34} \times 6.30 \times 10^{14} - 3.7 \times 10^{-19} = 4.769 \times 10^{-20}$ J

       $\frac{1}{2} mv_{max}^2 = 4.769 \times 10^{-20} \div 1.6 \times 10^{-19}$ eV = 0.298 eV ≈ 0.3 eV

  (iii)   0.3 V

2   (a) A photon is a discrete bundle (or quantum) of electromagnetic energy. It is often referred to as a *particle of light*.

  (b)(i)   Energy = $hf = \frac{hc}{\lambda} = 6.63 \times 10^{-34} \times 3 \times 10^8 \div 450 \times 10^{-9} = 4.42 \times 10^{-19}$ J

    (ii)   Number of photons per second = $50 \div 4.42 \times 10^{-19} = 1.13 \times 10^{20}$ s⁻¹

    (iii) $\frac{1}{2} \times 1.13 \times 10^{20}$ s⁻¹ = 5.66×10^{19} s⁻¹

    (iv)   Number of photoelectrons per second = $1 \times 10^{-6} \times 5.66 \times 10^{19} = 5.66 \times 10^{13}$ s⁻¹

    (v)   Charge per second = $5.66 \times 10^{13} \times 1.6 \times 10^{-19} = 9.05 \times 10^{-6}$ C s⁻¹

    (vi) 9.05×10^{-6} A

(c) None. The wavelength is greater than the upper wavelength (550 nm) for emission.

3   $E = hc \left(\dfrac{1}{\lambda} - \dfrac{1}{\lambda_o} \right)$

$$E = \underbrace{\left(hc \right)}_{m} \cdot \underbrace{\left(\dfrac{1}{\lambda} \right)}_{x} \underbrace{\left(-\dfrac{hc}{\lambda_o} \right)}_{+\,c} \quad \text{and comparing with}$$

$$y = $$

shows us that we should plot a graph of E on the vertical axis against $\dfrac{1}{\lambda}$ on horizontal axis (take care with the unit on horizontal axis). The graph has a gradient of hc and crosses the vertical axis at $-\dfrac{hc}{\lambda_o}$. The gradient, hc, should turn out to be approximately 1.8×10^{-25} Jm. Taking $c = 3 \times 10^8$ m s⁻¹ gives $h \approx 1.8 \times 10^{-25} \div 3 \times 10^8 = 6 \times 10^{-34}$ J s

The intercept on the vertical axis $\approx -3 \times 10^{-19}$ J, and since $\lambda_o = -hc \div$ intercept, this gives λ_o to be approximately 600 nm.

Exercise 2.5B

1   (a) Pass a ray of light from the Sun (or other incandescent source) through a triangular glass prism (or diffraction grating) and observe the image on a screen.

  (b)(i)   Pass a ray of light from a hydrogen discharge lamp through a triangular glass prism (or direct vision spectroscope) and observe the image.

    (ii)   An electron in an excited state relaxes by moving to a lower energy level and consequently a photon of energy corresponding to that transition is emitted.

    (iii) $E = \dfrac{hc}{\lambda} = (6.63 \times 10^{-34} \times 3 \times 10^8) \div 658 \times 10^{-9} = 3.023 \times 10^{-19}$ J

      $E = 3.023 \times 10^{-19} \div 1.6 \times 10^{-19}$ eV = 1.89 eV

      The electron therefore moves from the −1.51 eV energy level to the −3.40 eV energy level.

2   (a) An electron is in the ground state if it occupies the lowest possible energy level.

  (b) Energy difference = 13.6 − 3.40 = 10.2 eV

  (c) Maximum photon energy = 13.6 eV = $13.6 \times 1.6 \times 10^{-19}$ J = 2.176×10^{-18} J

    Photon frequency = $\dfrac{E}{h} = 2.176 \times 10^{-18} \div 6.63 \times 10^{-34} = 3.282 \times 10^{15}$ Hz

Minimum photon wavelength $= \dfrac{c}{f} = 3 \times 10^8 \div 3.282{\times}10^{15} = 91.4$ nm

Minimum photon energy $= 13.6 - 3.40$ eV $= 10.2 \times 1.6{\times}10^{-19}$ J $= 1.632{\times}10^{-18}$ J

Photon frequency $= \dfrac{E}{h} = 1.632{\times}10^{-18} \div 6.63{\times}10^{-34} = 2.462{\times}10^{15}$ Hz

Maximum photon wavelength $= \dfrac{c}{f} = 3{\times}10^8 \div 2.462{\times}10^{15} = 122$ nm

This range of photon wavelengths lies entirely within the UV region of the spectrum.

3 (a)

n	2	3	4	5	6
$1/n^2$	0.250	0.111	0.063	0.040	0.028
λ / nm	122	103	97	95	94
$^1/_\lambda$ / nm^{-1}	$8.20{\times}10^{-3}$	$9.71{\times}10^{-3}$	$10.0{\times}10^{-3}$	$10.5{\times}10^{-3}$	$10.6{\times}10^{-3}$

(b) and (c) By comparing given equation with $y = mx + c$, observe that:

(i)   the gradient of the graph of $\dfrac{1}{\lambda}$ (vertical axis) against $\dfrac{1}{n^2}$ is $-R$ and

(ii)   the intercept on vertical axis is R.

Both should show $R \approx 1.1{\times}10^7$ m^{-1}.

(For example, gradient $= \{(10.6{\times}10^{-3} - 8.20){\times}10^{-3}\} \div (0.028 - 0.250)$

$= -0.0108$ $nm^{-1} = -1.08{\times}10^7$ m^{-1}, so $R \approx 1.1{\times}10^7$ m^{-1} as required)

Exercise 2.5C

1 (a) See text page 155.

(b) Embed the target in a large mass of copper to conduct the heat away (from the target). Circulate cooling oil through the target.

(c) An incident electron encounters the extra-nuclear electrons of the target and rapidly slows down. The energy lost by the electron appears as an X-ray photon. An incident electron may lose varying amounts of energy in different encounters, so X-ray photons of different wavelengths are produced.

(d) An incident electron collides with an extra-nuclear electron in the target and knocks it out of its shell. An electron from a higher energy shell dropping down to a lower energy shell immediately fills the vacancy. This causes the emission of an X-ray photon, whose frequency depends on the difference in the energy levels involved. Different targets have shells with different energy levels, so a discrete spectrum is produced which is characteristic of that target.

(e) (i) $\lambda_{min} = \dfrac{hc}{eV} = (6.63{\times}10^{-34} \times 3{\times}10^8) \div (1.6{\times}10^{-19} \times 1{\times}10^5) \approx 1.24{\times}10^{-11}$ m

(ii)   Minimum wavelength unchanged, continuous spectrum similar to that for tungsten. Wavelengths of discrete lines different.

2 (a) See text page 157.

(b) *Cost:* CT scans can cost £150 or more. *Radiation:* CT scans can give a dose corresponding to around 100 conventional X-rays. The doctor has to ask if the benefits of CT scanning outweigh the possible danger of over exposure to X-rays. *Patient age:* Babies are particularly sensitive to X-rays and are generally not given a CT scan.

Exercise 2.6

1 (a) Letters (in order): W,W,W,W, P, E, E

   (b) See text on page 160.

2 (a) (i) From definition of KE, $v = \sqrt{\dfrac{2 \times KE}{m}} = \sqrt{\dfrac{2 \times 2.2 \times 10^{-18}}{9.11 \times 10^{-31}}} = 2.2 \times 10^6$ m s^{-1}

    (ii) $p = mv = 9.11 \times 10^{-31} \times 2.2 \times 10^6 = 2 \times 10^{-24}$ Ns

    (iii) $\lambda = \dfrac{h}{p} = (6.63 \times 10^{-34} \div 2 \times 10^{-24}) = 3.3 \times 10^{-10}$ m

   (b) $\lambda = \dfrac{h}{p} = (6.63 \times 10^{-34} \div 0.025 \times 400) = 6.63 \times 10^{-35}$ m,

    which is much too small to show diffraction.

3 $p = \dfrac{h}{\lambda} = 6.63 \times 10^{-34} \div 3.64 \times 10^{-10} = 1.82 \times 10^{-24}$ Ns

$m = \dfrac{p}{v} = 1.82 \times 10^{-24} \div 2 \times 10^6 = 9.11 \times 10^{-31}$ kg, which is the mass of an electron.

The particle is therefore likely to be an electron.

Exercise 2.7

1 When the car is approaching the observer, $\Delta\lambda = 3.4$ cm

$\lambda_1 = 50 - 3.4 = 46.6$ cm and $\lambda_2 = 50 + 3.4 = 53.4$ cm

$\dfrac{\Delta\lambda}{\lambda} = \dfrac{v}{c}$ so $\dfrac{3.4}{50} = \dfrac{\text{speed of car}}{\text{speed of sound}} = \dfrac{\text{speed of car}}{340}$

hence, speed of car = $(340 \times 3.4) \div 50 = 23.12$ m s^{-1}

2 First find the true wavelength of the sound source:

$\dfrac{\lambda - 1}{\lambda} = \dfrac{100}{350}$, so $350\lambda - 350 = 100\lambda$ giving $\lambda = 1.4$ m

Now find the true frequency:

$f = \dfrac{v}{\lambda} = \dfrac{350}{1.4} = 250$ Hz

3 $H = \dfrac{v}{d} = (75\,000$ m s$^{-1}) \div (3.26 \times 10^6 \times 9.46 \times 10^{15}$ m$) = 2.43 \times 10^{-18}$ s^{-1}

4 (a) $z = \dfrac{\Delta\lambda}{\lambda}$; $\dfrac{19.8}{396.8} = \dfrac{\Delta\lambda \text{ for K}}{393.4}$ so $\Delta\lambda$ for $K = \dfrac{19.8 \times 393.4}{396.8} = 19.6$ nm

    So λ for $K = 19.6 + 393.4 = 413$ nm

   (b) Using the H-line:

    Recession speed, $v = \dfrac{c \times \Delta\lambda}{\lambda} = \dfrac{3 \times 10^8 \times 19.8}{396.8} = 1.5 \times 10^7$ m s^{-1}

Exercise 3.1A

1 7.27 cm

2 4.03 cm

3 9.18 cm

Exercise 3.1B

1 3.56 cm

2 5.80 cm

3 7.72 cm

Exercise 3.3A

1 Max and Min method gives 25.5 to 16.3 to 11.8. $R = 16 \pm 7\ \Omega$
   Percentage uncertainty method gives $16.3 \pm 37.1\%$. $R = 16 \pm 6\ \Omega$

Exercise 3.3B

1 (a) The diagram (right) shows a workable circuit using correct symbols. A switch is not required since one is usually on the power supply.

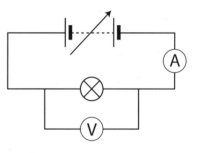

   (b) 1 Adjust power supply to a suitable value, for example, 2 V.
   2 Record the readings on the voltmeter and ammeter.
   3 Turn the voltage back to zero and adjust back to 2 V.
   4 Record the readings on the voltmeter and ammeter.
   5 Repeat until you have recorded three readings.
   6 Adjust the voltage to 4 V, 6 V, 8 V and 10 V.
   7 Repeat the procedure listed in steps 2 to 5.
   Your table of results should look similar to this:

V_1 / V	V_2 / V	V_3 / V	$V_{average}$ / V	I_1 / A	I_2 / A	I_3 / A	$I_{average}$ / A	R / Ω
2.0								
4.0								

   (c) Sketch the graph with resistance on the vertical axis and voltage on the horizontal axis.

2 (a) Your tables of results should look similar to this:

Time for A to break the beam			Average Time / s
T_1 / s	T_2 / s	T_3 / s	T_A

Time for B to break the beam			Average Time / s
T_1 / s	T_2 / s	T_3 / s	T_B

Time to travel from A to B			Average Time / s
T_1 / s	T_2 / s	T_3 / s	T_{AB}

(b) The width of the opaque section A and B is required to allow the velocity of the strip at A and B to be found.

(c) Velocity at A = width of A ÷ Average time T_A

Velocity at B = width of B ÷ Average time T_B.

$$\text{Acceleration of free fall} = \frac{\text{Velocity at B} - \text{Velocity at A}}{\text{Average time to move from A to B } (T_{AB})}$$

3 (a) and (b) To calculate the magnification you need to measure the height of the illuminated object (call it h_o) and the height of the image formed on the screen (call it h_i).

Measurements are repeated and an average taken. Deciding on when an image is sharp is a matter of judgement and so this requires repeat measurements. Find the position that gives a sharp image by moving the lens back and forth. Repeat until you feel the image is sharp. Three such measurements is sufficient.

Height of object h_o = _____ cm

Image distances / cm				Height of image / cm				Magnification $m = h_o \div h_i$
v_1	v_2	v_3	$v_{average}$	h_{i1}	h_{i2}	h_{i3}	$h_{i\,average}$	
2.0								
4.0								

(c) Substitute your values for image distance, $v_{average}$, and magnification, m, into the equation $m = \dfrac{v}{f} - 1$ and calculate an average value for the focal length, f.

4 (a) To calculate the volume of a steel ball bearing use the micrometer gauge.

Measure the diameter at a number of places and calculate the average diameter.

The micrometer can read to an accuracy of ± 0.01 mm.

If the ball bearing has a diameter of 10 mm then the uncertainty is $\dfrac{0.01}{10} \times 100 = 0.1\%$.

However, the volume of the sphere is $\dfrac{4}{3}\pi\left(\dfrac{d}{2}\right)^3$ so the uncertainty is 3 times, i.e. 0.3%.

(b) To calculate the volume of a glass microscope slide use both the vernier calliper and the micrometer gauge. Use the vernier calliper to measure the length and width of the slide. The thickness should then be measured using the micrometer gauge. Each of these measurements should be repeated a number of times and an average found.

A vernier calliper can read to an accuracy of ±0.1 mm and the micrometer can read to an accuracy of ±0.01 mm. If the microscope slide measures 50 mm × 20 mm × 2 mm

The uncertainties from vernier callipers are $\dfrac{0.1}{50} \times 100 = 0.2\%$ and $\dfrac{0.1}{20} \times 100 = 0.5\%$

The uncertainty from the micrometer gauge measurement is $\dfrac{0.1}{2} \times 100 = 0.5\%$

To find the volume the three measurements are multiplied and the overall uncertainty in the volume is the sum of the three uncertainties, i.e. 0.2% + 0.5% + 0.5% = 1.2%

(c) To measure the volume of a CD you will need the 30 cm rule and the micrometer gauge. The diameter of the CD is likely to be too large to fit inside the jaws of the vernier calliper so a 30 cm rule will have to be used. Use the ruler to measure the diameter in at least

6 places and take an average. The thickness of the CD is measured using the micrometer gauge. Again, make repeated measurements and obtain an average.

If the diameter of the CD is 120 mm ± 1 mm, uncertainty = $\dfrac{1}{120} \times 100 = 0.9\%$

If the thickness of the CD is 1.2 mm ± 0.01 mm, uncertainty = $\dfrac{0.01}{1.2} \times 100 = 0.9\%$

Volume of CD = area × thickness = $\pi\left(\dfrac{d}{2}\right)^2 \times$ thickness

Since the diameter needs squared, the uncertainty becomes 2 × 0.9% = 1.8%

Overall uncertainty in the volume measurement = 1.8 + 0.9 = 2.7%

5 (a) and (b) This means finding the position of balance for each weight, re-positioning it and finding the balance position again. It is important to repeat measurements.

(c) Your table of results should look similar to this:

W / N	D_1 / cm	D_2 / cm	D_3 / cm	$D_{average}$ / cm	F_1 / N	F_2 / N	F_3 / N	$F_{average}$ / N
2								
3								
4								

(d) To verify the Principle of Moments, present your calculations in a table to show that in each case the clockwise and anti-clockwise moments are the same.

W / N	$D_{average}$ / cm	Clockwise moment	F / N	45 cm	Anti-clockwise moment
2					
3					
4					

6 (a) To measure A trace around the prism, using a sharp pencil. Then use a protractor to measure the angle.

(b) Mark the light rays with a pencil, remove the prism and use a protractor to measure the angle. Record your angles of incidence and deviation in a table, similar to the one shown below. For each set of measurements calculate the refractive index.

Angle of incidence / °	Angle of deviation D / °	Refractive index n
30		
40		
50		

Average value for the refractive index n = _____

Exercise 3.3C

1 $\%\Delta V = \dfrac{0.2}{4.9} \times 100 = 4.1\%$ $\%\Delta I = \dfrac{0.01}{0.3} \times 100 = 3.3\%$ $\%\Delta R = 4.1 + 3.3 = 7.4\%$

Calculated value of $R = \dfrac{4.9}{0.3} = 16.3\ \Omega$, but $\Delta R = 1.2\ \Omega$ thus $R = 16.3 \pm 1.2\ \Omega$

2 (a) Plot a graph of (potential difference)^2 on the horizontal axis and power in watts on the vertical axis.

Potential difference² / V²	Power / W
0	0
0.25	0.06
1	0.25
2.25	0.575
4	1
6.25	1.56
9	2.25

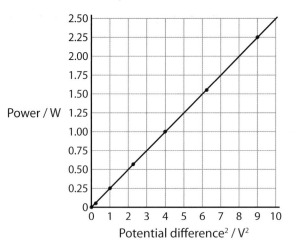

(b) Gradient = 1 ÷ R = 0.25, R = 4 Ω

3 (a) See graph on the right.

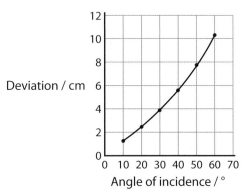

(b) $D = 0.39 + 0.067{\times}45 + 0.0015{\times}45^2 = 6.4$ cm

(c) Typically $\dfrac{(6.6 - 6.4)}{6.6} \times 100 = 3\%$

4 In this question it is important to convert all the uncertainties to percentages. Percentage uncertainties always add, even when the quantities are subtracted or divided.

(a) $\%\Delta m = \dfrac{1}{115} \times 100 = 1.7\%$

(b) $\%\Delta V_{water} = \dfrac{2}{60} \times 100 = 3.3\%$

(c) $\%\Delta V_{water+stone} = \dfrac{2}{130} \times 100 = 1.5\%$

(d) $V_{stone} = (130 \pm 2) - (60 \pm 2) = 70 \pm 4$ cm³ so $\% V_{stone} = \dfrac{4}{70} \times 100 = 5.7\%$

(e) Density $D = M \div V = \dfrac{115}{70} = 1.64$ g cm⁻³.

$\%\Delta D = \%\Delta m + \%\Delta V_{stone} = 1.7\% + 5.7\% = 7.4\%$

(f) Density = (1.64 ± 0.10) g cm⁻³

5 (a) See graph on the right.

(b) Graph should be a smooth curve with minimum between 39.30° and 39.35°.

(c) Take more measurements between angles of incidence 47° to 48°.

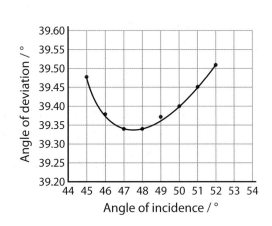

6 (a) The object has to be placed at a distance from the lens greater than this to obtain an image on the screen.

(b) The object distance should be the distance from the lens to the object.

(c) A mesh or tracing paper with a cross on it.

7 (a) To ensure the ball bearing is moving with constant velocity.

(b)

Radius of ball bearing / mm	5	8	10	12	15
Average time / s	5.7	2.2	1.4	1.1	0.7
Terminal velocity / cm s^{-1}	3.5	9.2	14.3	18.7	28.6

(c) C: $v = kr^2$

(d) $\dfrac{v}{r^2}$ = constant: $\dfrac{3.5}{25} = 0.14$, $\dfrac{9.2}{64} = 0.14$,

$\dfrac{14.3}{100} = 0.14$, $\dfrac{18.7}{144} = 0.13$, $\dfrac{25}{225} = 0.13$

You could also draw a graph.

The best-fit line on the graph is a straight line, therefore $\dfrac{v}{r^2}$ = constant.

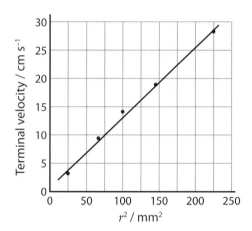

8 (a) to (d) Remember for an object staring from rest and moving with uniform acceleration, the final velocity is twice the average velocity. $v_{\text{average}} = \frac{1}{2}(u + v)$, $u = 0$

Height of the runway / cm	Time to travel 100 cm / s				Average speed / m s^{-1}	Final velocity / m s^{-1}	Acceleration	$\dfrac{\text{height}}{\text{acceleration}}$
	1st timing	2nd timing	3rd timing	Average time / s				
2.5	5.0	5.2	4.9	5.0	0.20	0.40	0.08	31.3
5.0	3.5	3.5	3.7	3.6	0.28	0.56	0.16	31.3
7.5	2.93	3.01	2.8	2.9	0.35	0.70	0.24	31.3
10.0	2.67	2.45	2.5	2.5	0.40	0.80	0.32	31.3
12.5	2.23	2.31	2.20	2.2	0.45	0.90	0.41	30.5

(e) A $a = kh$ for the range of measurements taken. The table shows that $h \div a$ = constant.

9 (a) Calculated from the graph, gradient = 1.2 A

(b) For $N = 1$, $I = 1.2$ A. Therefore $R = V \div I = 6.0 \div 1.2 = 5.0\ \Omega$

(c) $I = 1.2N$

10 (a) Uncertainty in each reading is ± 0.5 mm

Diameter = 15 mm, %Δdiameter = 6.7%

(b) Volume = $\dfrac{4}{3}\pi r^3 = 1.8$ cm^3, %Δvolume = $3 \times 6.7 = 20\%$

(c) $\%\Delta\text{mass} = \dfrac{1}{15} \times 100 = 7\%$

(d) Calculated value of density $= \dfrac{15}{1.76} = 8.3$ g cm^{-3}

   $\%\Delta\text{Density} = 20 + 7 = 27\%$, which is 2.2 g cm^{-3}

   Therefore density $= (8.3 \pm 2.2)$ g cm^{-3}

11 (a)

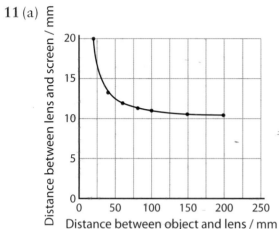

(b) Estimate of focal length = 10 cm.

   Explanation: as the object is moved further away, i.e. as it approaches infinity, the image is formed at the focal point.

Copyright

Copyright has been acknowledged to the best of our ability. If there are any inadvertent errors or omissions, we shall be happy to correct them in any future editions.

Credits

Unless stated below, all images are © Pat Carson, Roy White and Colourpoint Creative Ltd. The following photographs, diagrams, graphs and tables are all included with the kind permission of the copyright holders. The numbers denote page numbers.

Apollo 17 crew, NASA	41
Authors	174, 178, 179, 181
iStockPhoto	84 (both), 90, 156 (both bottom right), 157 (top), 158 (both), cover
NASA/ESA and The Hubble Heritage Team STScI/AURA	167
Wesley Johnston	171 (top)